THEY

HELPED

MAKE

America

FAN KISSEN

Houghton Mifflin Company BOSTON

The Riverside Press Cambridge

Illustrations by Cheslie d'Andrea

Contents

Willian

Brother to All Men

CAST

JOHN ASHTON	WILLIAM PENN
EDWARD THOMSON	KING CHARLES II
MRS. THOMSON	DUKE OF YORK
MR. ROBERTS	LORD BERKELEY
MRS. ROBERTS	SIR GEORGE CARTERET
CAPTAIN	SARAH
SOLDIER 1	HARRY
SOLDIER 2	DEBORAH
SOLDIER 3	MAYOR OF NEW CASTLE
SOLDIER 4	WILLIAM MARKHAM

SCENE 1

Time: 1672

Place: A street in London

(*A Friends' meeting house, a simple building, is at the back of the stage. John Ashton and Mr. and Mrs. Thomson enter and walk to the meeting house door. As they talk, other Friends arrive, singly and by twos.*)

ASHTON: We're very early, Friend Thomson. (*He tries the knob of the door.*) The door is still locked.

THOMSON: That's strange, Friend Ashton.
Friend George West is always here to unlock
the door long before meeting time.

MRS. THOMSON: Thee has a key, Edward. Thee can open
the door for us.

(*Thomson looks in his pocket for the key.*)

ROBERTS: Why are you waiting outside, Friends?

ASHTON: The door is still locked, as thee can see, Friend
Roberts.

MRS. ROBERTS: Locked? But it's time for the meeting to
start.

THOMSON: (*Angrily*) This is not our own lock! This is a
padlock!

ASHTON: (*Going closer*) It's the King's padlock! The
King's coat of arms is on it!

MRS. THOMSON: Another meeting house of the Friends
barred and padlocked!

THOMSON: We can't hold our meeting!

ASHTON: The King's men have locked our meeting house!

MRS. ROBERTS: Our meeting house on the other side of the
river was burned to the ground by the King's orders!

ASHTON: The King may lock our meeting houses or burn
them down or throw us into jail, but he can never make
us give up our beliefs!

THOMSON: (*Looking to one side*) Look! The soldiers are coming!

VOICES: Soldiers! The King's men!

(*Enter a small group of soldiers, headed by a captain.*)

CAPTAIN: What are all you people doing here?

ASHTON: We came here to hold a meeting.

CAPTAIN: That's forbidden. It's the King's orders. You Quakers are forbidden to hold meetings.

ROBERTS: We don't like to be called Quakers, if you please. We are members of the Society of Friends of the Truth.

SOLDIER 1: Who cares what you call yourselves? Quakers, we call you.

SOLDIER 2: The King has no love for you Quakers, with your bold *thee* and *thou* to everyone.

SOLDIER 3: It's reported that William Penn said *thee* even to King Charles himself.

SOLDIER 4: If I were his Majesty, I'd have clapped William Penn into jail for that, even if he is the son of Admiral Penn.

MRS. ROBERTS: Friend William Penn has been in jail several times for his beliefs. The King can't frighten him.

CAPTAIN: Enough of this chatter! Break up this unlawful gathering! Go home, all of you!

THOMSON: Unlawful? We are simple, peaceful people, who have come together to worship according to our beliefs.

CAPTAIN: (*Touches his forehead*) You're simple, all right! Don't you know about the new law? It's against the law now to worship in any church except the Church of England. You may not hold any other religious beliefs. Go home now, all of you, or I'll have to arrest you!

7

(*William Penn enters. He walks into the midst of the group of Friends.*)

PENN: What's the trouble, Friends?

THOMSON: The King's men have padlocked our meeting house, Friend Penn.

CAPTAIN: So this is William Penn, the most troublesome Quaker of the lot of you!

PENN: I've done nothing but stand up for my beliefs as one of the Society of Friends.

CAPTAIN: You should know that those beliefs are forbidden now. The King's law says you must worship only according to the Church of England.

PENN: The King may make any laws he chooses. He can close or burn a meeting house. But he can't control a man's conscience. We Friends will continue to worship according to our own beliefs.

CAPTAIN: And where will you hold your meetings, now that all places of worship are padlocked, except Church of England buildings?

PENN: We don't need a building. We can hold our meetings anywhere, even outdoors. Cheer up, Friends. We'll hold our meeting right here in the street, since our meeting house is locked.

CAPTAIN: William Penn, I arrest you, in the King's name!

PENN: What for? What's the charge against me?

CAPTAIN: For holding an unlawful meeting and making speeches against the law of the land.

PENN: But I haven't said a word against the law!

CAPTAIN: You've said enough! You're a Quaker, and you're about to hold a Quaker meeting. That's unlawful. The Lord Mayor of London was sure you'd try that soon, so he gave the order for your arrest.

SOLDIER I : What have you to say for yourself now, William Penn? If you don't change your religion, you'll die in jail!

PENN: My prison shall be my grave before I change my beliefs one bit. My conscience is my own, and I will not go against it for any man. I'm ready for your jail, Captain.

SCENE 2

Time: March 4, 1681
Place: Audience room of King Charles II

(*King Charles sits in a tall chair. The Duke of York, brother of the King, and Lord Berkeley and Sir George Carteret stand beside him. A chair and a table with writing materials are at one side. A soldier stands guard at a door at each end of the room.*)

KING: Lord Berkeley and Sir George, I've called you here to tell you what I plan to do about William Penn's request for land.

9

YORK: And of course, brother Charles, you expect these gentlemen to tell you that you're doing the right thing.

KING: (*Smiles*) Naturally, James.   The King can do no wrong!

BERKELEY: Has your Majesty decided to grant Penn's request and give him the land he wants in America?

KING: Yes. After thinking it over for a few years, . . .

YORK: (*Interrupts with a smile*) The King thinks slowly.

KING: (*Smiles*) Don't interrupt, James! As I was about to say, after thinking it over for a few years, I've decided I'll be making a good bargain by granting William Penn land in America as payment of what I owed his father. I owed Admiral Sir William Penn a matter of sixteen thousand English pounds.   I could never pay his son this amount in cash.

YORK: Very clever, Charles! Land in the wilds of the New World costs you nothing.

KING: Exactly! I pay what I owe, which makes me an honest man, but at no cost to myself.

CARTERET: A very clever bargain on your part, your Majesty!

KING: Oh, there's more to my clever bargain, Sir George. I am at the same time getting rid of a great nuisance.

BERKELEY: Meaning, your Majesty, the troublesome Quakers?

KING: And William Penn himself! How well you understand me, my good friends! Penn wants the land to set up homes for the Quakers. Well, he may have the land, and the right to become its Governor.

YORK: For once in your life, Charles, you're doing a wise thing. I admire William Penn, in spite of his beliefs.

CARTERET: Shall I have Penn called in, your Majesty? He's waiting in the outer room.

KING: Yes, Sir George.

(*Carteret takes a few steps toward the soldier at one of the doors.*)

CARTERET: (*Raises his voice a bit*) Soldier! Tell Mr. Penn that his Majesty will see him now.

(*The soldier salutes and goes out. He returns almost immediately, followed by William Penn. Penn is wearing his hat.*)

BERKELEY: (*Sharply, to Penn*) Remove your hat, Penn! You are in the presence of his Majesty, the King, and three noblemen!

PENN: (*Calmly*) No, my Lord Berkeley. I won't remove my hat either for the King or for you. We Friends don't remove our hats for any man merely because he is rich or a nobleman. We believe all men should be shown equal respect.

KING: (*Smiling*) Let him be, Berkeley. He's stubborn enough in his Quaker beliefs to go to jail for them, and none of us can change him.

CARTERET: Your Majesty is altogether too easy and patient with him.

KING: It's because of his father, the Admiral, who did England a great service during the war with the Dutch. The son shows his father's courage and brave heart, though in a different cause. Well, to business! William Penn, I've decided to grant you the land you asked for.

PENN: I'm very grateful to your Majesty. I've long dreamed of setting up a home in America for the Friends and for others who are unhappy in their own country. May I ask just where this tract of land is, your Majesty?

KING: The charter is on the table, there. Bring it here, Sir George, and let Penn read where the land lies.

(*Carteret takes the charter off the table and unrolls it. He and Penn examine it.*)

CARTERET: It's a piece of land almost as large as England itself, Penn. It's this area west of the Delaware River.

PENN: There are rivers flowing through the land, so it should be good for farming, and a pleasant place to live.

KING: I've given a name to your new land, Penn, as you can see if you read further.

PENN: (*Reads*) "This land shall be called *Pennsylvania*." (*Upset*) But I intended to call it merely *Sylvania*, meaning *woods*!

KING: And what's the matter with *Pennsylvania*?

PENN: That sounds as if I were naming the land after myself, in my own honor. I don't want anyone to believe I
would be so vain.

KING: I want to honor your father, not you. You may tell
anybody who calls you vain that the colony was named
by the King in honor of Admiral Sir William Penn.
Pennsylvania it shall be!

YORK: How soon do you intend to leave England, Penn?

PENN: I shall send a large group of colonists out as soon as
possible. As for myself, I have much to do before I
leave. I want as many people as possible to know of this
new colony, and so I shall spread a description of it
throughout England and all the countries in Europe.

YORK: What sort of people do you believe will join you
out there in the wilderness of America?

PENN: Men and women to whom freedom of thought is so precious that they will be willing to struggle for a time in a new land. I want good and honest workmen of every trade. In my description of the country I shall tell of the chances to make a good living there. But I shall also warn people that they must be ready to give up many comforts for a time in exchange for freedom.

KING: I wish you luck, William Penn. It sounds as if your colony of Pennsylvania should be a great success. It will be a good thing for England to have another rich colony in America.

PENN: This grant of land to the Friends is a great and just act, your Majesty. God will, I believe, bless the colony.

SCENE 3

Time: November, 1682
Place: Open ground at New Castle, on the Delaware

(Groups of men and women stand or walk about. At the back of the stage is a raised platform with a table on it.)

SARAH: Thee will never know, Friend Deborah, how glad we were to set foot on dry land again. Such a hard time we had on board the *Welcome*, from the time we left England!

HARRY: It's a small ship, as thee can see by looking down the river. The colonists filled it with all sorts of tools for farming, for their trades, and for building houses.

14

MRS. ROBERTS: And our household goods, too — cupboards and beds and cooking pots and our precious personal belongings.

DEBORAH: Naturally, Friend Martha. Without our personal things, simple as these may be, a house is not a home.

ROBERTS: Besides all this, the ship carried all the food we would need for two months and some cows, chickens and geese.

DEBORAH: I can see how very crowded the passengers must have been.

SARAH: The worst of the voyage was something we had not expected to carry — smallpox!

DEBORAH: Smallpox! That cruel disease!

HARRY: There were a hundred of us who left England in the *Welcome*. Thirty-one of these died of the disease and had to be buried at sea.

DEBORAH: That must have been terrible! We Friends who came here earlier with Friend Penn's cousin, William Markham, are glad we can give you a place to rest until you can build homes of your own.

ROBERTS: Here comes Friend William Penn now.

DEBORAH: And the Mayor of New Castle.

MRS. ROBERTS: And William Markham.

(*Enter William Penn, William Markham, and the Mayor of New Castle. They mount the platform and take their places behind the table. There are sounds of pleasure from the people in the crowd.*)

VOICES: Welcome, Friend William Penn! Our new Governor has come at last!

(*The Mayor raises his hand for silence.*)

MAYOR: Friends of the new colony of Pennsylvania, we meet here to greet and welcome the man who is to be the new Governor of our colony.

VOICES: Long live William Penn! Welcome, William Penn!

MAYOR: The new Governor brings you a letter from his Majesty, King Charles the Second of England. (*He holds up the letter*.) His Majesty declares this land is to be called Pennsylvania. He orders all the people now settled here to give all obedience to William Penn. He is declared to be owner and Governor of this tract of land, with all the powers of owner and Governor.

VOICES: Long live Friend Penn! Long live Governor Penn!

MAYOR: And now, step forward, William Penn, so that you may take office as Governor according to our custom. Receive the turf and twig, water and soil, of the land. (*As the Mayor mentions each article, he hands it to Penn, who holds it up for the people to see, then puts it back on the table*.) William Penn, take this dish of grassy earth from the ground that now is yours. This twig is from the trees that grow on your land. This water stands for the rivers that flow through your land. This damp soil is the bottom of the River Delaware. And now, William Penn, you are master of all the land, and all that feeds and grows on the land, the rivers that flow through it, and all that sails or lives in the rivers. Long live William Penn, Governor of Pennsylvania!

A
LETTER
FROM
William Penn
Proprietary and Governour of
PENNSYLVANIA

As alfo an Account of the CITY of
PHILADELPHIA
Newly laid out.
Its Scituation between two Navigable Rivers, Delaware and Skulkill

VOICES: Long live William Penn, Governor of Pennsylvania!

PENN: My friends, I hope you will be happy under my government. I have not come here to seek wealth for myself by laying heavy taxes on you. I shall make it my duty to give you a fair and honest government, with equal rights and freedom for all.

VOICES: Hear! Hear! Right, Friend Penn!

PENN; I intend that this colony shall be governed by a Council of men chosen by yourselves. In this way you will be governed by laws of your own making.

ROBERTS: Then there'll be no cruel and unjust laws!

PENN: Here in Pennsylvania every man shall be free to worship in whatever church he may choose.

VOICES: Freedom of worship! At last! At last!

MARKHAM: Friends, Governor Penn also has ideas for building a town.

PENN: Yes, I've made plans for a great town beside the river. It shall have straight, wide streets, and large lots, so that each house may have land around it. It shall be a green, country town. I've decided to call it

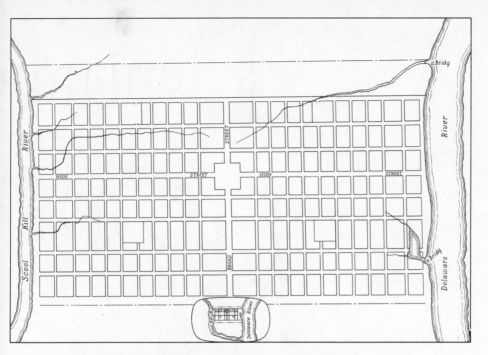

Philadelphia, the City of Brotherly Love.

ROBERTS: The City of Brotherly Love! This sounds good, Friend Penn. But what about the Indians? Will they let us live here in peace?

PENN: The success of this colony depends on our friendship with the Indians. We must be just and honorable in our dealings with our red brothers. We must show them that we want to gain and hold their friendship.

HARRY: And I believe thee will show us the way, Friend Penn!

PENN: My first task here is to make a treaty with the Indians. I shall set out at once to visit their villages and make friends with their chiefs, so that we can arrange a meeting for a peace treaty. And while I am busy making peace with the Indians, you, my friends, will start building Philadelphia, the City of Brotherly Love.

THE END

Benjamin

ranklin

Statesman and Inventor

CAST

NARRATOR	MR. WOODS
BENJAMIN FRANKLIN	MR. ELLIS
JAMES FRANKLIN	MR. FARR
MR. CHASE	FIRST MAN
MRS. CHASE	OLD MAN
FIRST SOLDIER	YOUNG MAN
SECOND SOLDIER	FIRST WOMAN
WILLIAM FRANKLIN	SECOND WOMAN
THE SPEAKER	THIRD WOMAN

THE CLERK AND MEMBERS OF THE HOUSE OF COMMONS

(The stage curtain is down. The narrator steps out in front of it.)

#1 NARRATOR: Greetings, friends! I'd like to tell you just a little about Benjamin Franklin. The story of everything he did would fill many books.

In his day Ben Franklin's name was known in every household in America, and in much of Europe, too. The American colonists sometimes called him Poor Richard, after *Poor Richard's Almanack*, which he published every year for twenty-five years. The almanac was filled with wise sayings that are repeated even today.

21

#2 Narrator: Ben Franklin's life was a long and busy one, spent in the service of all the American colonists. He believed all the colonists had the same problems facing them. He thought of them as Americans, living together in one country. That's why he has been called the first true American.

It's hard to believe that a man who became a newspaper publisher, writer, scientist, inventor, and statesman went to school only until the age of ten. Two years later he became an apprentice in the printing shop of his older brother James in Boston. But young Ben and his brother didn't get along very well.

(Narrator steps off the stage, and the curtain goes up.)

SCENE 1

Time: 1722
Place: Printing shop of James Franklin

(Front room of the printing shop of James Franklin. Newspapers are stacked on a table. At one end of the table young Ben Franklin sits reading a book. After a few moments James Franklin enters. Ben doesn't notice this.)

JAMES: Ben! *(Slight pause)* Ben!

BEN: *(Looks up from his book)* Oh! Excuse me, James. I didn't hear you come in.

JAMES: *(Angry)* You've got your nose in a book again, you lazy boy!

BEN: It's a little early for customers, so I thought I'd finish this grammar I borrowed last night.

JAMES: I'm sure you could have found something to do at the printing press instead of wasting time on a book. But you've always been lazy. I remember the time you floated on your back in the water with a big kite in your hand, letting the wind pull you along. Too lazy to use your arms and legs to swim!

BEN: That wasn't laziness, James. I was experimenting, to see if the wind could hold up a man and pull him along. It was a scientific experiment.

JAMES: You and your scientific experiments! And now it's a grammar. What's so wonderful about a grammar?

BEN: Why, it helps me put words together properly, so I can make people understand exactly what I mean.

JAMES: So you plan to be a writer? (*Laughs in a mean way*) Perhaps you don't like the way I run the paper. Perhaps you're planning to print it yourself!

BEN: I didn't say that, James. You're always finding fault with me for things I haven't said or done. You're my brother, not my master, James.

JAMES: (*Angry*) Why, you lazy, vain ——!

(*The door opens. Mr. and Mrs. Chase enter.*)

MR. CHASE: Good morning, Mr. Franklin. Good morning, Ben.

JAMES: Good morning, Mr. Chase. How are you, Mrs. Chase?

MRS. CHASE: Very well, thank you. And how are you, young Ben? Still reading books?

BEN: Whenever I can borrow them, Mrs. Chase.

MR. CHASE: We happened to be passing this way, and we stopped in to buy the latest copy of your paper.

JAMES: Certainly, Mr. Chase. Two copies, as usual?

MRS. CHASE: Oh, yes, Mr. Franklin. I always send one to my brother in New York. He likes to read the letters of Mrs. Silence Dogood. I hope there's one of her letters in this week's paper?

JAMES: Yes, there is, Mrs. Chase. (*He gives a copy of the paper to her and one to her husband.*)

MR. CHASE: You know, Mr. Franklin, I strongly suspect that Silence Dogood is not a woman at all. Is it really true that you don't know who she is, or do you refuse to tell your readers?

JAMES: I really don't know who Mrs. Dogood is, Mr. Chase. I've asked her, in the paper, to come here, but she never has.

BEN: We find her letters in the morning, slipped under the door of the shop. She said, in her first one, that she thinks newspaper articles are dull, so she has set out to make them entertaining.

MRS. CHASE: There's nothing dull about Mrs. Dogood's letters!

MR. CHASE: But under that entertaining way of writing there's very serious meaning. When she's not pointing out some way we can improve ourselves, she is telling the government how it can do better.

MRS. CHASE: She finds fault with what she calls the "silly fashions of women's clothes," too, so she just can't be a woman.

JAMES: Maybe Mrs. Silence Dogood is a man, Mrs. Chase. Yet I don't know of any man who can write such masterpieces of good sense and good English.

MR. CHASE: You'd better watch out. One of these days Mrs. Dogood's letters finding fault with the government will get you and your paper into trouble.

JAMES: I'll take my chances, Mr. Chase, as long as her articles continue to delight the readers of my paper.

MRS. CHASE: Well, we must be running along. Good day, Mr. Franklin. Goodbye, young Ben. If you keep on reading those books, I shouldn't be surprised if you owned a paper of your own some day.

BEN: Perhaps I shall, Mrs. Chase. I'd like nothing better. (*Mr. and Mrs. Chase leave.*)

JAMES: There! Even Mrs. Chase could see how silly you are! Own your own paper! Huh!

BEN: But I was only thinking ——

JAMES: You weren't hired to think, but to work! Go back into the press room, Ben, and set up the report of his Majesty's last speech in London.

BEN: Very well, James.

(*As he turns to walk off, a sheet of paper falls out of his pocket. James picks it up and starts reading.*)

JAMES: Ben! What's this? (*Ben turns back.*) This letter! It's Mrs. Dogood's handwriting. But the letter isn't finished. She wouldn't leave an unfinished letter under our door. How did you get it? (*Sudden suspicion*) Ben! How did this letter get into your pocket?

BEN: (*Confused*) Well — I — I

JAMES: (*Very angry*) Ben! *You* are Mrs. Silence Dogood! You disguised your handwriting and wrote those letters under that name!

BEN: Yes, James. I wrote those letters.

JAMES: How dared you do such a thing behind my back!

BEN: You wouldn't have printed them if you had known I wrote them. But the readers of the paper like the letters. You know that. Why do you object now?

JAMES: Why do I object? Why, you stupid young fool! Your attacks on the government have made plenty of enemies for my paper.

BEN: But we've made more friends, James. Lots of people admire your paper for printing the truth.

JAMES: This last letter of yours will surely get us into trouble with the Governor. You make fun of his failure to send ships against the pirates, and you call his ship captains "butterflies."

BEN: I wanted to force him to make up his mind and act. You agreed with what my letter said, or you wouldn't have printed it.

JAMES: That was because I didn't know who ——

(*The door opens. Two soldiers enter.*)

FIRST SOLDIER: James Franklin?

JAMES: Yes, I am James Franklin.

FIRST SOLDIER: You are under arrest.

JAMES: What for? I've done nothing against the law.

SECOND SOLDIER: You attacked the Governor in your newspaper.

JAMES: But — we have freedom of the press here!

SECOND SOLDIER: Explain that to the court and the Governor. Come along!

CURTAIN

(Narrator steps in front of the curtain.)

#3 NARRATOR: Well, James Franklin spent a few months in prison for printing Silence Dogood's attack on the governor. During that time young Ben Franklin kept his brother's paper going. When James was freed, Ben decided he couldn't get along with his brother any longer. So he ran off to Philadelphia.

This was the beginning of a new life for Ben Franklin. After some years he began to publish the *Pennsylvania Gazette* and *Poor Richard's Almanack*. Both of these were a great success. To add to Ben's good fortune, he married Deborah Read, whom he had met on his arrival in Philadelphia.

#4 Narrator: As the years passed, Ben Franklin became more and more interested in science. Perhaps his greatest interest was in electricity, about which very little was known at that time.

Have you heard the story of his experiment with the kite, and what it meant? That happened when Ben's son William was about twenty years old.

(The narrator steps off the stage as the curtain goes up.)

SCENE 2

Time: A summer day, 1752
Place: Inside a large shed in the fields

(The shed was once a cow shed. Some farming tools and empty milk pails stand against the walls. There is a large window without glass in the rear wall. Ben Franklin and his son William, about 20, enter rapidly. Ben is holding a large kite.)

WILLIAM: Well, we reached the shed before the rain, Father.

BEN: And without anyone's seeing us, Billy.

WILLIAM: I certainly would have felt silly if any friend of mine had seen me. Imagine going out to fly a kite when a thunderstorm is about to break!

BEN: I would have been much annoyed, too, Billy, but for quite another reason. I don't want anyone to know about this experiment of mine. Not yet, anyhow.

WILLIAM: You asked me to help you, Father, but I'm not sure I know just what you're after.

BEN: It's not hard to understand, son. You know I've been studying what the scientists here and in Europe have been doing to learn more about electricity. For my part, I feel sure that lightning and electricity are the same thing, that lightning *is* electricity. That's what I'm hoping this experiment of mine will prove.

WILLIAM: But how will flying a kite in a thunder and lightning storm prove it?

BEN: I'll explain while you help me. Here, tie the end of this string to my kite.

(*They suit their actions to the words.*)

I want the kite to go very high, high enough to touch one of those thunder clouds we can see gathering in the sky.

WILLIAM: This string seems long enough. There must be about a thousand feet of string in this ball. And why did you make the kite of silk?

BEN: That's simple enough, William. A paper kite would be soaked through and would fall apart in no time. Silk is light and strong.

WILLIAM: I should have thought of that myself!

BEN: Now we'll tie this piece·of narrow silk ribbon to the end of the kite string.

WILLIAM: That's done.

BEN: (*Takes a very big key out of his pocket.*) And now I'll tie this iron door key at the place where the silk ribbon is tied to the kite string. So!

WILLIAM: What's this sharp, pointed wire at the top of the kite for, Father?

BEN: This sharp wire is the whole point of my experiment, Billy. I want to get the wire close to the lightning. The lightning may hit the wire.

WILLIAM: Suppose the lightning does hit this wire? How will you know it's the same as electricity?

BEN: Why, if it's electricity, it will travel down the wet string and into this iron key, and I'll feel an electric shock. That will prove that lightning is electricity. (*A flash of lightning is seen through the window, followed a few seconds later by the rumble of thunder.*)

WILLIAM: (*Excited*) The storm is breaking, Father!

BEN: (*Excited*) Let's put the kite out of the open window and send it up into the clouds! (*They put the kite through the window and look up into the sky.*)

WILLIAM: The wind's carrying it straight up into the air, Father, right toward that heavy thunder cloud!

(*Another flash of lightning, followed by thunder*)

BEN: That one missed it. Maybe it will be hit by the next one. But there *is* electricity in the air, Billy! I can see the little hairs on this silk string standing out stiff!

WILLIAM: The clouds are rolling in heavier and lower now.
　　(*Another flash of lightning, followed by thunder*)
BEN: That lightning was right over the kite! (*He starts
　　back with a cry.*) Oh! I felt a shock in my hand! I had
　　my finger on the door key, and I felt an electric shock,
　　Billy! The lightning struck the wire point on the kite,
　　then it traveled down the wet string, and hit the key!
　　Billy, the lightning *is* electricity!
WILLIAM: (*Excited*) Did you really feel an electric shock
　　Father?
BEN: I did! I know I did, Billy! (*He jumps back as an-
　　other flash of lightning is seen through the window.*) An-
　　other shock! I felt it again, Billy! I'm right! Light-
　　ning is electricity!

WILLIAM: Give me the kite string, Father. Let me feel the electric shock from the lightning.

BEN: (*Emphatic*) No! I won't!

WILLIAM: (*Surprised*) Why not?

BEN: I won't let you risk it. Scientists know very little, so far, about electricity. I may be doing a very risky and foolish thing, drawing the lightning from the sky. It may be just luck that the shock didn't kill me.

WILLIAM: (*Thoughtful*) You may be right, Father. People have been struck by lightning and killed.

BEN: And houses struck by lightning have burned to the ground.

WILLIAM: Well, Father, after this kite experiment of yours, you won't catch me holding anything made of iron in my hand when I'm out in a thunderstorm.

BEN: (*Very serious*) Billy! This sharp wire point on my kite gives me an idea for an invention!

WILLIAM: Everything seems to give you an idea for an invention!

BEN: (*Slowly, thinking it out*) Suppose a building had a long metal rod from its roof down into the ground. Then this metal rod could catch the lightning and carry the electricity down into the ground. The electricity wouldn't touch the building. The rod would protect the building from lightning!

WILLIAM: (*Excited*) A lightning protector!

BEN: That's it, Billy! A metal rod on a building would be a lightning protector. Think how many buildings would be saved each year by a lightning protector!

WILLIAM: An ounce of prevention is worth a pound of cure, Father, as Poor Richard says.

BEN: Right!

WILLIAM: You can make a lot of money on a lightning protector. Will you patent this invention, Father, so nobody else can make it or sell it?

BEN: No, Billy. I've never patented any of my inventions, as you know. I believe any idea that may help others should belong to everybody. Let's pull in our kite now and go home. (*He starts pulling in the kite.*) I've proved my idea that lightning and electricity are the same, and I've thought of another invention, too — a lightning rod. I'd call this experiment a great success.

CURTAIN

(*The narrator steps before the curtain again.*)

#5 NARRATOR: Well, Ben's kite experiment was written up in all the science journals in America and Europe. It made the name of Ben Franklin even more famous.

But science was only one side of Ben Franklin's life. The people of all the American colonies soon came to recognize him as a wise and able man. So it was not surprising that the Pennsylvania colonists called upon him to go to England to settle a disagreement between them and the sons of William Penn, who were still the owners of the land granted to Penn.

#6 Narrator: While Franklin was in England, Parliament passed the Stamp Act. This act made it necessary for the colonists to pay to have government stamps put on all legal papers and even newspapers. This stamp tax made the colonists very angry. To show their anger, they stopped buying many kinds of goods which they had been buying from English merchants.

Of course, the English merchants didn't like losing

34

their business with the colonies, and they began to think that the Stamp Act was a bad law.   They let members of Parliament know what they thought about it, too.

When the House of Commons met to consider repealing the Stamp Act, Franklin was still in England, and he was questioned on the feelings of the American colonists.
(The narrator steps off the stage.)

SCENE 3

Time: July 3, 1766
Place: The House of Commons, London

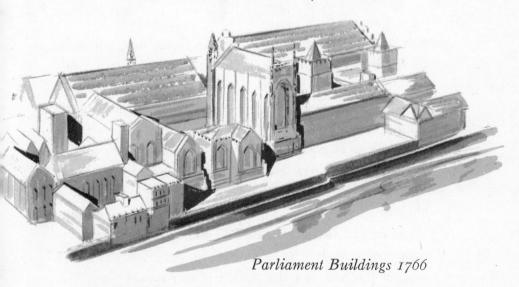

Parliament Buildings 1766

(The Speaker's desk is on a platform at the back of the stage.   A clerk sits at a desk just below this.   At each side, from front to rear, and facing towards the center, sit the members of the House of Commons. The Speaker of the House enters.   The members rise as he takes his place at his desk.)

SPEAKER: Gentlemen of the House of Commons, you may be seated. (*The members take their seats.*)

Gentlemen, the business of the day is the examination of Mr. Benjamin Franklin. The clerk of the House will kindly call Mr. Franklin. (*The clerk goes out. He returns almost immediately, followed by Benjamin Franklin. As Franklin enters, some of the members clap and cheer. The Speaker frowns and raps his gavel.*)

Gentlemen! We all know that Mr. Franklin is a great scientist and inventor. But he stands here now as the agent of the King's colonists in America. This is neither the time nor the place to cheer him. Now, Mr. Franklin, kindly take your place at the desk, sir. (*Franklin stands beside the clerk's desk, then bows to the members at each side.*) Mr. Franklin, you are here to explain the actions of your fellow colonists. They are refusing to buy our English goods.

FRANKLIN: And we shall continue to do without English goods as long as we must pay unfair taxes.

SPEAKER: Don't you believe that the colonists should pay a share of the cost of the French and Indian Wars?

FRANKLIN: Certainly, sir. The colonists don't object to paying a reasonable share of those costs.

SPEAKER: Then why won't they pay the Stamp Tax to raise the money? Why have they stopped buying English goods?

FRANKLIN: We object strongly to the manner in which this tax was decided upon. We were not consulted at all when Parliament passed the Stamp Act.

SPEAKER: (*Scornful*) Why should we consult you colonists? Don't you believe that Parliament is the judge of what should be done, what laws should be passed?

FRANKLIN: The members of Parliament have the right to speak their minds. But the colonists believe that Parliament should not pass any laws that concern us without letting us be heard.

WOODS: (*Rises in his seat.*) Mr. Speaker, may I ask Mr. Franklin a question?

SPEAKER: You may, Mr. Woods.

WOODS: Mr. Franklin, what feelings did the colonists have towards Parliament before this Stamp Act was passed?

FRANKLIN: Only feelings of the greatest respect, sir. Since the members of Parliament are chosen by the people, the colonists have always thought of Parliament as the champion and protector of the people.

WOODS: And how do the colonists feel towards us now?

FRANKLIN: Our feelings are very much changed! You have set up taxes, without giving our representatives the chance to be heard. We feel that taxation without representation is tyranny, sir!

VOICES: (*Approving*) Hear! Hear!

37

ELLIS: (*Rises, to Speaker*) May I ask a question, sir? (*The Speaker nods.*) Mr. Franklin, do you believe the colonists will buy English goods if we cut the tax a bit?

FRANKLIN: Never, sir! The colonists will never pay this tax!

ELLIS: The articles we sell to you are necessary to you colonists. You must buy them from England. You can't get along without them.

FRANKLIN: We believe we can get along without them. We'll gladly do without rather than pay an unjust tax. There isn't a single article that we are now buying from England that we can't do without or make ourselves.

FARR: (*Rises*) Mr. Franklin, suppose England should decide to send soldiers to make the American colonists pay the tax? What then? You'd have to pay it.

Franklin: Oh? What will your soldiers do? They can't force a man to buy something if he doesn't choose to buy it. We Americans are not armed. Your soldiers will not find us ready to fight. (*He pauses to let his words sink in.*) But — if you send soldiers over, you might force us to fight!

FARR: Mr. Franklin, you keep saying "we Americans," and "we colonists." You think of yourself as one of them?

FRANKLIN: Certainly, sir.

FARR: We must believe, then, that you, too, defy the King and Parliament, that you, too, defy England.

FRANKLIN: No, sir! I do not defy the King or Parliament, as you are trying to make me say. I respect the King. So do most of the colonists. We are Englishmen who want to make America a colony that England can be proud of.

VOICES: (*Approving*) Hear! Hear!

FRANKLIN: But if the King continues to be stubborn, if Parliament continues to tax us without consulting us, how can we remain true to England?

VOICES: Rebel! He's a rebel, like the rest of them!

SPEAKER: Mr. Franklin, do you believe the Americans would dare to revolt against England?

FRANKLIN: Dare, sir? We are Englishmen, like you. We would dare much for our liberty. We Americans ask only to have the same rights as Englishmen living here in England. We're tired of hearing the King called "our master," as if we were slaves, of having to obey laws we had no part in making. Treat us like fellow Englishmen! Then we'll gladly work along with you.

FARR: You are rebels, not Englishmen!

VOICES: Rebels! All rebels!

FRANKLIN: (*Quietly*) There are some colonists who are ready to forget that they are Englishmen. Laws like the Stamp Act will force more to do so. Lift the tax! Give us a voice in the laws made for us!

WOODS: Mr. Speaker and gentlemen of the House! Mr. Franklin has presented a strong case for the American colonists. It is possible that Parliament has made a mistake in passing the Stamp Act. I move that Mr. Franklin be asked to leave while we talk over the matter of lifting the tax.

VOICES: (*In approval and disapproval*) Hear! Hear! No! No! They're rebels! Vote! Let's vote!

SPEAKER: (*Raps his gavel.*) Gentlemen! Gentlemen! (*The members quiet down.*) Mr. Franklin, you are excused for today.

CURTAIN

(The narrator comes before the curtain.)

#7 NARRATOR: So well did Benjamin Franklin speak for the American colonists that Parliament did lift the hated stamp tax. But later, while Franklin was still in England, other laws were passed that made the colonists angry. Finally it came to the point where British soldiers fired on some Americans. The Americans fired back. Then Ben Franklin realized that there was nothing more he could do. Sadly he returned to America. He found that war had started.

#8 Narrator: Franklin was an old man by that time, but his mind was clear and active. He became a member of the new Congress and was one of the men asked to draw up the Declaration of Independence when the colonies decided to become a free nation. This very young nation needed money and arms to keep up its fight against England. Benjamin Franklin, as the wisest and most famous American, was sent to France to ask for help. When the war was over, it was a very tired but very happy Benjamin Franklin who came home to the cheers of his grateful countrymen.

(The narrator steps off the stage.)

SCENE 4

Time: September, 1785
Place: The street in front of Franklin's house, Philadelphia

(The front of Franklin's house appears at the back of the stage. People move back and forth slowly in front of the house. Here and there are small groups.)

FIRST MAN: (*To small group near him*). I wonder if Ben Franklin has changed his ways since he's been living in France among dukes and kings?

OLD MAN: No, Ben Franklin would never change his ways. Why, I fought Indians and helped build forts with him during the war. Franklin was a rich man even then, but he worked and joked with us common soldiers as if he were one of us.

YOUNG MAN: Ben Franklin's always been for the common man. Lots of rich men stuck to the King and called the rest of us rebels. But Franklin worked for our rights. He's always stood for the good of all Americans.

FIRST WOMAN: We women are thankful to Ben Franklin, too. He's the man who invented a stove to keep our houses warm.

SECOND WOMAN: It was his idea to pave the streets and keep the mud out of our houses every time it rains.

THIRD WOMAN: And he's the one who started the fire fighting companies. (*Church bells are heard off stage.*)

YOUNG MAN: Listen! The church bells! Franklin's ship must have tied up to the dock!

OLD MAN: That's the same dock where he landed from Boston as a poor young man more than sixty years ago. (*Cheers are heard, coming closer — "Franklin! Ben Franklin!"*)

FIRST WOMAN: Listen to the cheers! He's coming!

SECOND WOMAN: Here he comes! Here's Ben Franklin! (*The people on the street make room for the approaching crowd. Franklin enters, waving his hat to the cheering crowd which is following him. He stops in front of the house as the crowd presses around him.*)

VOICES: Franklin! Ben Franklin! Hurray for Ben Franklin!

THE END

43

P au

Revere

Patriot and Craftsman

CAST

FATHER   JOSEPH REVERE
DICK MASON   MR. WILLIAM CARVER
MR. EVE   MARIA REVERE
PAUL REVERE   HARRIET REVERE
RACHEL, his wife   ELLA
MRS. ABBIE CARVER   CAPTAIN DERBY
                MR. WILLIAM RITCHIE

Time: Today
Place: Dick Mason's home

(*The curtain is down. In front of it Dick sits at a table piled with school books. He looks into an open book for a few seconds, then away, as if memorizing something. Enter Dick's father, carrying a briefcase and newspaper.*)

FATHER: Hi, there, Dick! Hard at work, I see!

DICK: (*Looks up from book*) Hello, Dad! Yes, I'm getting an early start on the homework.

FATHER: Good for you! Say, that looks like a book of poetry. Are you memorizing a poem? (*He puts briefcase and newspaper on the table and looks at the book.*)

45

DICK: *Paul Revere's Ride.* Want to hear me?

> "Listen, my children, and you shall hear
> Of the midnight ride of Paul Revere,
> On the eighteenth of April, in Seventy-five;"

FATHER: (*Takes it up*) "Hardly a man is now alive

> Who remembers that famous day and year.
> He said to his friend, 'If the British march
> By land or sea from the town tonight,
> Hang a lantern aloft in the belfry arch
> Of the North Church tower as a signal light — '"

I could say it in my sleep, Dick.

DICK: Did you learn this poem in school, too, Dad?

FATHER: I certainly did. And since then I've read a little more about Paul Revere and his times. You know, I've wondered why people remember only that ride of his. He did a lot of other important things. but folks often forget, or else don't know about many of them.

DICK: Why, what else did he do? Other important things — I always think of him as the man who warned the Americans that the British were on the way to attack them.

FATHER: Oh, Paul Revere was much more than just the messenger who carried that warning. He served as a regular soldier during the Revolutionary War. And did you know that he was the cleverest Yankee craftsman of his time? He was also well-known for thinking up new ways of making many things. Once, when the colonists needed gunpowder and didn't know how to make it, they turned to Paul Revere for help . . .

(Dick and Father walk off stage at side as Father is finishing last line. The table is removed and the curtain goes up.)

SCENE 1

Time: 1776

Place: Office of Oswell Eve's powder mill outside Philadelphia

(*Mr. Eve is sitting at his desk. There is a knock at the door.*)

EVE: Come in!

(*Paul Revere enters and walks to Mr. Eve's desk.*)

REVERE: Good morning, Mr. Eve. I am Paul Revere, from Boston.

EVE: Revere? Oh, yes. Sit down, won't you? I've heard your name. You've been carrying messages from the Boston rebels . . .

REVERE: (*Breaking in*) Patriots, if you please, Mr. Eve!

EVE: Depends on how you look at it, Mr. Revere. But you're the one who carries information back and forth between the New England leaders and the Continental Congress here in Philadelphia. What can I do for you?

REVERE: Our Continental army is in great need of gunpowder, especially in New England. And you, Mr. Eve, have the best powder mill in America.

EVE: (*Proudly*) That's a well-known fact. Then you are here to buy my gunpowder?

REVERE: Not exactly. I'm not here to buy your powder. I've come to learn how you make it — how your mill is set up — everything you do.

EVE: (*Astounded*) What!

REVERE: You see, the Continental Congress has decided to set up a powder mill at Canton, near Boston. I've been asked to set up a mill and start making the powder as quickly as possible.

EVE: You're a silversmith, I've heard. Yet you dare try to start a gunpowder mill without any experience at it?

REVERE: I know something of working with metals, Mr. Eve. Besides, I'm ready to try anything if it will help America.

EVE: But how will you go about making the powder? You need saltpeter. That's the most important material. Do you suppose England will ship her saltpeter to the Boston rebels?

REVERE: I must correct you again, Mr. Eve. Patriots, if you please. We need not count on England. We find we are able to produce saltpeter here at home.

EVE: (*Angry*) But — but such impudence! Why should I teach you how to make gunpowder? Why should I help another mill compete with me in my own business?

REVERE: (*Takes out several letters and hands them to Mr. Eve.*) I have some letters here from leaders of the Continental Congress. They hoped you would help me.

EVE: (*Opens the letters and glances at the names of the writers.*) James Otis, John Hancock, Robert Morris. Let's see what Mr. Morris has to say. "I hope you will cheerfully and from public spirit give Mr. Revere such information as will enable him to conduct the business of building a powder mill and making gunpowder on his return home." Out of public spirit! Hmph! Suppose the British succeed in stopping this revolt? Where will this public spirit put me with the British then, Mr. Revere?

REVERE: We Americans will win this fight, Mr. Eve! Each of us must do his share, so that we can really become a nation of free men.

EVE: Well, I can't refuse a request made by James Otis or Robert Morris. I'll show you my mill, Mr. Revere.

REVERE: Let me spend a week or two examining the machinery and learning how to make the powder.

EVE: (*Angry*) A week or two! Most certainly not! I'm a very busy man. I'll walk through the mill with you, and you can see the machines and watch the way they work for just a few minutes. But there's to be no questioning of my workmen! I won't give away all my trade secrets. I can spare you an hour, or a little longer.

REVERE: An hour, to learn how to set up machinery for a powder mill and learn how to make gunpowder? Surely you're joking, Mr. Eve.

EVE: I am not joking. I must honor Mr. Morris' request to give you some information, but you must learn whatever you can in the time I can spare you. (*Rises and walks toward the door*) Come along, Mr. Revere. Just one hour!

CURTAIN

(*Dick and his father step out at side of curtain.*)

DICK: Well, Dad, that didn't give Paul Revere much chance to learn how to make gunpowder. What happened?

FATHER: Fortunately for the patriots, Dick, Paul Revere had a sharp eye and a good memory. He used both. From what he saw he was able to draw plans for a powder mill and start making powder. He even learned to make cannons.

DICK: And was that the end of his worries as a patriot?

FATHER: Not by a long shot, Dick. When the war was ended, Paul Revere went back to his silver shop. Soon, however, our country had new problems, and again Paul Revere was asked to help solve them. (*Dick and Father begin to walk off stage.*) In 1794 the sign over his shop read *Paul Revere and Son.*

SCENE 2

Time: 1794
Place: Show room of silver shop of *Paul Revere and Son.*

(*Mrs. Rachel Revere and Mrs. Abbie Carver are examining a silver water pitcher. Paul and Joseph Revere are standing behind the counter.*)

RACHEL: Here it is, Abbie. This is the pitcher I wanted you to see. It's Paul's latest design. How do you like it?

MRS. CARVER: It's a handsome pitcher, Rachel.

JOSEPH: Don't you think its simple, slender shape is graceful, Mrs. Carver?

MRS. CARVER: Yes, it's very graceful, Joseph. (*Doubtful*) But I'm not sure I like it well enough to buy it. It's ... well, it's a bit too plain for my tastes.

REVERE: Plain, Abbie? Why, look at this fine grape design running around the top and down the handle.

MRS. CARVER: It's pretty, Paul, but it's too simple. I like the designs you used to make before the war. You know, bunches of roses and little angels. It was all so rich and elegant.

REVERE: You mean the fancy English designs we used to copy?

MRS. CARVER: Yes, that's it. Why don't you keep on copying the English designs, Paul?

REVERE: I've stopped imitating English fashions, Abbie. We Americans live a different life now. We're developing new ways of our own.

JOSEPH: That's why Father and I like to make simple American designs.

MRS. CARVER: Well, I don't see any harm in continuing to imitate England, even if we are independent now.

REVERE: That's just it! America must be independent in every way, not only as a government. We must be able to make anything we want or need. We're clever enough to figure out ways of doing it.

RACHEL: (*Proudly*) Just as you figured out how to make gunpowder and cannons, Paul.

JOSEPH: Even though Father was a silversmith by trade, Mrs. Carver.

MRS. CARVER: Well, that was during the war. Times are different now.

REVERE: Are times different now, Abbie? We're at war now, too. We've been fighting an undeclared war against France for the past few years, you know. France has been seizing our ships and keeping them in her ports or using them in her fight against England.

JOSEPH: And the North African pirates do worse than that, Mrs. Carver. They've been capturing our ships and keeping our sailors as slaves.

MRS. CARVER: Pirates! Oh, dear me! The very word frightens me! (*The doorbell tinkles as Mr. Carver comes in and closes the door quickly. It is plain that he is upset about something.*) Why, William! What's the matter? You look terribly upset. What's wrong?

MR. CARVER: Upset! I should think I *am* upset, Abbie. (*To the Reveres*) Excuse me for bursting in like this. Have you heard the latest news?

REVERE: No, William. Joseph and I have been indoors all afternoon.

MR. CARVER: There's a merchant ship just in from the south of France. Her captain says he barely managed to escape from an African pirate ship.

REVERE: It's lucky for him that he did escape!

MR. CARVER: Lucky for *him!* But he says he saw them capture another American ship, *The Flying Arrow.*

MRS. CARVER: *The Flying Arrow!* Oh, dear me! That's your ship, William!

MR. CARVER: Yes, it's my ship. And her captain's Ahab Perkins, one of the finest in New England, with a fine crew, too. My ship is captured — my goods all stolen by those pirates! I'm ruined!

JOSEPH: And all those American seamen carried off as slaves! It's a disgrace!

RACHEL: Why does President Washington stand for this? He's a brave soldier. He's never run away from a fight.

REVERE: It's because our government is still weak, Rachel. We have no navy, no warships to send after those pirates.

MR. CARVER: It's even worse than that. Our government has agreed to pay the ruler of that pirate country a million dollars in one lump sum, and twenty thousand dollars every year besides, to leave our ships and sailors alone. But they still seize our ships and men.

JOSEPH: It's disgraceful to pay those pirates! We can't trust their word.

MR. CARVER: Their ruler laughs at us. You've heard what he said, "If you pay me tribute each year, you are my slaves." Americans, slaves! No wonder we're crying, "Millions for defense, not one penny for tribute!"

REVERE: I say we can't live unless our ships and sailors are free to go anywhere without being stopped. We must have freedom of the seas.

MR. CARVER: Those pirates have taken my ship! I'm ruined!

MRS. CARVER: There, there, William. Try not to be so upset about it. I'm sure you'll find a way to make up your losses. Let's go home and you can get some rest.

MR. CARVER: Perhaps I'd better go home, Abbie. I'm sure I can't get any work done now.

RACHEL: Good day, William, Abbie.

REVERE: We'll find a way to beat those pirates soon, William. I'm certain of that.

(*The doorbell tinkles as Mr. and Mrs. Carver leave.*)

RACHEL: I'd better go home too. Now, don't you two stay here till all hours, as usual.

REVERE: We'll try to get home early, Rachel.

(*Rachel leaves. Doorbell tinkles.*)

JOSEPH: What makes you so certain that we'll beat those pirates soon, Father?

REVERE: I learned a short time ago that the government is planning to build six warships. Without telling you, Joseph, I put in a bid to supply all the brass and copper fittings. Today I received a letter telling me that my bid has been accepted. (*Proudly*) *Paul Revere and Son* is to supply the fittings for American Navy ships.

JOSEPH: (*Dismayed*) But, Father! We don't know how to make brass and copper hard enough for bolts and spikes. That's a secret known only in England, and even there only a few men know it.

REVERE: That's true, just now.

JOSEPH: Even if we could do it, we'd have to get the metal from England. The way England feels toward us now, she probably won't sell us all we'll need for our work.

REVERE: Listen, Joseph! America must learn to get on without depending on any other country. It's time we learned to produce our own brass and copper. As for the secret of making it, we'll experiment, you and I, until we find it. We'll try over and over again, till we've mastered the skill. America needs brass and copper, and *Paul Revere and Son* will produce it!

CURTAIN

(*Dick and his Father step before the curtain again.*)

FATHER: So Paul Revere experimented until he was able to produce the brass and copper they needed for making bolts and spikes and other ship fittings. Then another ship problem came along for Paul Revere to solve.

DICK: What was that, Dad?

FATHER: It was something else about the use of copper. This problem came up about ten years later — in 1803. (*Dick and Father leave stage during last line above.*)

SCENE 3

Time: 1803

Place: Sitting room of Paul Revere's home

(*Paul and Joseph are sitting at a small table, looking over some business papers. Rachel holds an open book. Maria and Harriet sit nearby, reading or sewing. (There is a light knock at the door. Ella enters.*)

ELLA: Excuse me, Ma'am. There's a sea captain at the door. He says he's an old friend, Captain Elias Derby. Shall I let him in?

DERBY: (*Passes by Ella in doorway, smiling*) It's all right! I'm an honest man. You can't keep me from seeing my old friends, the Reveres. I'm back! How is everybody?
(*The Reveres all stand to greet Captain Derby.*)

REVERE: Welcome home, Elias! It's a long time since we saw you last in Boston.

RACHEL: It's good to see you again, Captain Elias. Sit down, and tell us where you've been.
(*They all sit down.*)

DERBY: Thank you, ma'am. I've been gone nearly two years this time. I declare, these girls of yours have grown up pretty as a picture.

RACHEL: (*Smiles*) Now, Elias, don't go making them vain.

JOSEPH: Where did you take *The Grand Turk* this time, Captain Derby?

DERBY: To China and the islands of the East again, Joseph.

REVERE: We Yankees up here are mighty proud of you and your ship. She's the first New England vessel that ever made that dangerous trip around the Horn and across to China.

RACHEL: And what did you bring back this time, Captain Elias?

DERBY: Chinese silks, and fine cups and bowls, cocoanuts, spices, and a few monkeys.

MARIA: Monkeys!

DERBY: Would you girls like a baby monkey as a pet? Or are you too old for such nonsense now?

HARRIET: Oh, no! I'd love it, Captain Derby!

58

MARIA: Mother, would you mind if we took it?

RACHEL: (*Laughs*) Well, a monkey couldn't get into much more mischief than you children used to. Yes, you may have the monkey, since Captain Derby is kind enough to offer it to you.

DERBY: Then I'll bring it around tomorrow morning.

HARRIET: Thank you, Captain Derby!

MARIA: Oh, thank you! We'll take good care of it.

DERBY: I've brought a china bowl for you, Rachel.

RACHEL: How nice of you to remember me! Thank you. And now I must get you a bit of dinner. Come, girls.

(*Harriet and Maria go off with Rachel.*)

REVERE: How was this trip, Elias?

DERBY: Very good, Paul. This trip was a successful one. I stand to make a good profit. (*Troubled*) But, I don't know how many more trips I'll be making to China, at least, in *The Grand Turk*.

JOSEPH: Why? You're not thinking of selling that fine ship, are you?

DERBY: *The Grand Turk* was a fine ship, Joseph. But she's sailed in salt water for a good spell now. The timbers of her hull are beginning to rot.

JOSEPH: Can't anything be done about that? You paint the hull often enough, I'm sure.

DERBY: Yes, but paint isn't enough. The tiny sea animals fasten themselves onto the wooden bottoms of the ships. That's what makes the timbers rot, and slows up the speed of the ship, too. What we need is a metal covering — a thin sheet of metal to nail over the wooden hull.

REVERE: Well, sheets of iron would rust in the water. Why not use sheet copper?

DERBY: Sheet copper? That's for warships, Paul. Besides, sheet copper would be too expensive for me.

REVERE: Some of the bigger merchant ships have sheets of copper over their hulls. It's expensive, though, as you say, Elias. Rolling copper into thin yet strong sheets is still an English trade secret, and our sheet copper has to come from England.

JOSEPH: The worst of it is, Captain Derby, England is still angry with us for breaking away from her, and she herself is at war with France. So our supply of rolled copper from England may be shut off any time.

REVERE: America's greatest wealth is in her merchant ships. We must find a way to prevent them from rotting, as well as to save them from the North African pirates.

DERBY: I can see why your mind is on the pirates just now, Paul. I hear that the government is repairing some of our warships to send out after them. Are you doing any of that repair work?

REVERE: Yes. I made the fittings for those ships when they were first built, and I'm mighty proud of them. The *Constitution* is my favorite ship. We'll have to put new copper sheeting on her hulls. I'm about to order some from England. (*He stops suddenly, slaps his hand down on the table.*) No, by George! I won't depend on England for that rolled copper!

JOSEPH: Where else can you get it, Father?

REVERE: I'll make my own rolled copper, right here in America!

JOSEPH: But how, Father? It's never been done in America before. We don't know how.

REVERE: I'll experiment, Joseph, till I learn how.

JOSEPH: But where will you carry on your experiments, Father? There's not an inch of extra space in our buildings.

REVERE: I'll put up a new building, to serve as a copper rolling mill.

JOSEPH: A new building! We haven't the money for that! Your experiments will be very costly.

REVERE: I'll get together every penny I own, and then I'll borrow.

DERBY: Why should you do it, Paul? You're sixty-eight years old. You're too old to start a new business, or to sink your last penny into something that's never been tried in America before.

REVERE: I feel I must, Elias. America is calling for my help again. If I can make our ships more seaworthy and better able to fight for us, I shall be helping America to win the freedom of the seas.

With our ships free to go anywhere, America will be on the way to take her place among the great nations of the world.

CURTAIN

(*Dick and Father come out before curtain.*)

DICK: And did Paul Revere find the way to make rolled copper, Dad?

FATHER: Yes, Dick, he did. Why, the *Constitution* was sheathed in just eleven days with sheet copper made in America. And a few years later Paul Revere had cause to be proud of his work. (*He and Dick walk off stage.*) It was August of 1812.

The Constitution

SCENE 4

Time: August, 1812
Place: Sitting room of the Revere home in Canton

(*Paul, Rachel, and Joseph Revere and Mr. William Ritchie are sitting and chatting in friendly fashion.*)

MR. RITCHIE: This new house of yours is mighty comfortable, Mrs. Revere.

RACHEL: Yes, we like it here in Canton, though our house is a little smaller than the Boston one.

REVERE: Since our silver shop and bell foundry and copper mill are all in Canton now, William, there's no reason why the family should remain in Boston.

63

MR. RITCHIE: Silversmith, bell caster, the first man to produce sheet copper in America — and that's not nearly all! You're the cleverest Yankee New England has ever produced, Paul! What a busy life you've led!

JOSEPH: I'm trying to get Father to give up business now, Mr. Ritchie. But he refuses to stop.

RACHEL: Paul's seventy-seven now, you know, William. He's earned a rest, if any man has.

MR. RITCHIE: You know you can depend on Joseph to carry on the business, Paul. Why do you still go to the foundry every day?

REVERE: Because I'm interested in all the work that goes on there. We've done so many things. We've even made some copper boilers for a strange ship that has no sails.

MR. RITCHIE: What? A ship without sails? How can it move?

REVERE: It's a curious ship built by a man named Robert Fulton, and it runs by the steam in its boilers. He claims the engines can push the ship along without the use of any sails at all.

MR. RITCHIE: What nonsense! Steam engines may help a ship when the wind dies down, but you'll never get me to believe that a steam engine alone can move a ship any distance.

REVERE: Ships! My talk always gets around to ships. They're the cause of our new war with England, you know. If England hadn't kept on stopping our ships and taking off our American seamen to help her fight France, we wouldn't be fighting her now.

JOSEPH: Well, Father, we Reveres can be proud of one thing. The fittings and copper sheathing of many a ship that's fighting for us have been made by *Paul Revere and Son.*

(*Loud ringing of bells is heard off stage. All sit up in surprise and wonder.*)

REVERE: Listen! The church bells! The courthouse bell! What do you suppose they are ringing for?

(*Harriet enters quickly, excited.*)

RACHEL: Harriet! What are the bells for?

HARRIET: Such wonderful news! The *Constitution* has defeated the English ship, the *Guerriere*, in a battle at sea!

REVERE: The *Constitution*! She's one of the ships we fitted out!

MR. RITCHIE: An American warship has defeated an English one! This certainly calls for cheers and the ringing of all the bells in America!

REVERE: The *Constitution! Paul Revere and Son* made the fittings for her when she was first built. We made the copper sheathing for her hull. And now she has won a victory for America! A Revere ship is making the seas safe for all American ships!

THE END

George

Washington

Father of His Country

CAST

HENRY	GENERAL GREENE
MARY	COLONEL HAMILTON
BESS	HAWKINS
JOHN	COLONEL RAHL
UNCLE JOE	FIRST MAN
TOMMY	FIRST OFFICER
PETE	SECOND OFFICER
BILL	FIRST WOMAN
HARRY	SECOND MAN
GEORGE WASHINGTON	SECOND WOMAN
MERCER	THIRD WOMAN
	KNOX

Time: April 30, 1789
Place: A street in New York

(*People are hurrying along in one direction. They talk as they move along.*)

HENRY: We'd better hurry, Mary, if we want a place where we can see everything that goes on.

MARY: I'm glad we live in New York, Henry. Imagine! We can see the first President of the United States take the oath of office!

BESS: Come on, John! Let's try to squeeze our way into the front of the crowd.

JOHN: You'll see him clearly, Bess. General Washington will be taking the oath of office up on the balcony of Federal Hall. That'll be up above the crowd.

(*Tommy and Uncle Joe walk in more slowly. Uncle Joe limps. They stop about the center of the stage.*)

UNCLE: I'll have to stop a minute, Tommy, to rest my bad leg. An old soldier like me can't walk as fast as a young fellow like you.

TOMMY: I'm sorry, Uncle Joe. I didn't mean to hurry you. Only — we've come a long way to see Washington take office, and we don't want to miss any of it.

UNCLE: No need to rush. We're lucky that we're going to have a seat at the window of a house right opposite Federal Hall. You know I wouldn't want to miss any of it, either, Tommy. Why, I fought with General Washington as far back as the wars with the French and Indians, when he was only a young Colonel in Virginia.

TOMMY: And you fought right through this war with him, till the Battle of Yorktown. No wonder you're proud to see him President!

UNCLE: Proud! Our whole country's proud of General George Washington! He was the greatest man in the war. He's smart as a whip, and he out-smarted the British commanders lots of times, when he had only half as many men as they had. The British called him the "Old Fox," you know. (*He puts a hand on Tommy's shoulder, and the two start walking off.*) Why, I remember how it was at Trenton that Christmas night.

SCENE 1

Time: December 25, 1776
Place: Washington's camp at McKonkey's Ferry, on the Pennsylvania shore of the Delaware River

(*Soldiers' tents are seen in the background. Several soldiers are talking together. Now and then they walk slowly back and forth, or stop to beat their arms across their chests to keep warm.*)

JOE: Brrr! It's mighty cold today, Pete!

PETE: It's Christmas Day, Joe. What do you expect? July heat?

BILL: Christmas! It's not much of a holiday for us here.

HARRY: A bit of stringy meat and a spoonful of potatoes! A fine Christmas dinner that was!

BILL: I wish I'd had sense enough not to join this miserable bunch of men Washington calls his army. I wish I were home, in the warm kitchen of my own farmhouse.

PETE: That's where I'd like to be, too. We go hungry day after day. We freeze in our thin uniforms. What did I ever enlist for, I wonder?

JOE: To fight for your freedom, Pete! That's what you're
fighting for! For your liberty! For your right to live
under the laws you yourself make! Do you want a
stupid King and Parliament, thousands of miles away,
to make laws for us, and slap taxes on us, without letting
us have any say?

HARRY: Of course we don't, Joe. · That's why I enlisted,
up in Boston.

PETE: Sure! That's why I enlisted, too — to fight for
my freedom and for liberty. But how does Congress
expect us to fight when we're freezing and starving?

BILL: Pete's right in that. Congress is in charge of the
army, but never sends any supplies to keep us men
going.

HARRY: Not enough food, not enough guns or bullets.

PETE: I don't remember the last time we got paid.

BILL: Look at my feet! I had to tie rags around my shoes
to keep from being barefoot altogether. I can't blame
the men who desert. Brrr! I'm freezing!

JOE: Hold on there, Bill! You men are mighty sorry for
yourselves. In lots of ways you've got a right to complain. But you never heard General Washington saying
he's sorry for himself. The General's uniform isn't any
warmer than your own. He's a rich man. He could
have stayed in his own comfortable home down in Virginia. But he eats the same food we eat, and fights
alongside the rest of us.

PETE: I know he refused to take any pay for being Commander in Chief.

HARRY: Sure! General Washington's always ready to
share our hardships.

BILL: I know all that, too, boys. It's on account of him
that I'm sticking to the army. If it weren't for him, I'd
be home tonight.

PETE: All the same, I wish we were having as much fun
tonight as the British, over on the other side of the river.

HARRY: I'll bet they're celebrating Christmas with plenty
of cheer.

JOE: Those troops over by Trenton are mostly Hessians. They were hired by the British king. They're fighting for money. You and I and the rest of our army are fighting for our own country. We're Americans now, Pete. We've declared ourselves free! We're fighting to keep our independence as a nation.

BILL: Maybe our Declaration wasn't such a wise thing. Suppose the British beat us in this war?

JOE: No talk about losing, Bill! We'll win this war! General Washington will find a way to win!

PETE: He'll have to try mighty hard, with this ragged army. We've been licked in one battle after another.

HARRY: General Washington must have some special plan in mind right now. He's called a meeting with his other generals. There's General Greene going into his headquarters.

BILL: General Mercer and General Knox went in a little while ago. Colonel Hamilton's always with Washington.

HARRY: I bet the Hessian commander isn't thinking of plans to attack right now. I bet he and his officers are eating and dancing — along with the Americans who are still loyal to King George.

BILL: Dancing and making merry! That's what we should be doing on Christmas Day.

PETE: (*Looks up at the sky*) It's beginning to snow again. As if it weren't miserable enough!

HARRY: Well, that means we're sure to stay where we are, for tonight anyhow. The generals will never order an attack in this kind of weather.

JOE: Let's go into our tents and keep as warm and dry as we can. We can grumble just as well under cover.

SCENE 2

Time: The same as Scene 1
Place: Inside General Washington's headquarters
at McKonkey's Ferry

*(General Washington is seated at the center of a table,
with the other generals on each side. Colonel Hamilton stands a little behind Washington. There's a
window at the back of the room and a door at one
side.)*

WASHINGTON: Gentlemen, I've called you together to go
over the plans for the attack on Trenton. We attack
tonight.

MERCER: Tonight, General Washington? Do you believe it's wise to try crossing the river in this weather?

KNOX: (*Points to window*) The snow is beginning to change to icy rain, and the river's full of floating cakes of ice.

WASHINGTON: We start moving tonight, General Knox, as soon as it grows dark!

GREENE: Wouldn't it be just as well to wait till morning, General Washington? Our small boats may be broken to bits by the floating ice if we can't see where we're going. Even if we get across safely, we'll have to march eight miles over frozen ground through this storm.

WASHINGTON: We must take that chance, General Greene. We dare not sit here and wait till the British and Hessians are ready to attack us.

MERCER: It seems to me, General Washington, that we're risking another defeat if we try an attack on Trenton tonight. Our army isn't strong enough to stand up against that large force of British and Hessians.

WASHINGTON: It's true that we're not strong enough. That's why we must use our wits in place of extra men. Our hope lies in surprising the enemy.

HAMILTON: That's General Washington's strong point, gentlemen — using his wits to take the enemy by surprise. That's how he saved the army from capture on Long Island, you remember.

KNOX: We were defeated there, as I need not remind you, Colonel Hamilton. We risk another defeat tonight.

WASHINGTON: The Hessians won't be expecting an attack at Christmas time and in this weather, General Knox. They're celebrating over in Trenton. They'll sleep heavily afterwards. I'm counting on taking them by surprise early tomorrow morning.

74

HAMILTON: (*Breaking in*) Excuse me, gentlemen! Quiet for a moment, please. (*All watch him as he moves swiftly to the door and throws it open. Hawkins is standing outside. He holds an empty tray in his hands. Hamilton speaks sharply to him.*) What are you doing here, Hawkins?

HAWKINS: (*Salutes*) Excuse me, Colonel Hamilton. I only wanted to ask if General Washington or the other gentlemen wanted anything.

HAMILTON: (*Sharply*) No! If anything is wanted, I'll call you. General Washington is holding a conference. No one is to come near this room, not even you. Do you understand?

HAWKINS: Yes, sir. I'm sorry, Colonel Hamilton. (*He salutes and closes the door.*)

GREENE: Who is that man?

HAMILTON: Private George Hawkins, General Washington's orderly.

MERCER: Does he always stand outside your door, General Washington? Is he to be trusted?

WASHINGTON: He came to me with a letter from a member of Congress.

MERCER: A member of Congress! Hm! I wouldn't trust some of those men in Congress any farther than I can see. I'm sure some of them are still loyal to King George.

WASHINGTON: (*Discouraged*) I sometimes wonder about that myself, General Mercer. Congress is so backward about sending supplies and money for our army. I've sent letter after letter, begging our Congress for food and warm clothing and war supplies, but all I get is blame for losing battles.

HAMILTON: (*Angry*) It's the work of men who are jealous of you, General Washington! Some of our generals would like to be Commander in Chief in your place. They've been telling Congress that our army is much bigger than it really is, and that we have plenty of supplies. Those officers are putting the blame on you personally. They're jealous of you, General!

WASHINGTON: (*Tired*) If any other general wants my job as Commander in Chief, he may have it. I told Congress when I was first appointed that I didn't want it.

HAMILTON: And you told them you'd take no pay, except your expenses.

WASHINGTON: (*Angry*) I don't care much what people say against me, though it's discouraging enough. But I won't have them talk against the men in our army. Our men are freezing and starving, but they're keeping up their courage because they're fighting for liberty.

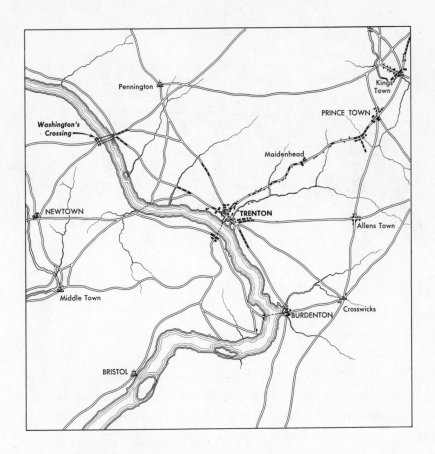

MERCER: And you're still set on sending these men to attack the British on this miserable night, General Washington?

WASHINGTON: Yes, General Mercer. I'm counting on a surprise attack for victory. We must have a victory, gentlemen, to cheer not only our soldiers but the whole country. It isn't our soldiers alone who are discouraged and down-hearted. Our people are beginning to doubt if we can ever defeat the British. We must show them that we can win! We must attack Trenton tonight! Gentlemen, it's victory or death!

SCENE 3

Time: Later that night
Place: A ballroom in a wealthy house in Trenton

(*The room is decorated for a Christmas party. A number of men and women move about, talking to each other. Most of the men are in the red British uniforms. The women are well-dressed. The Hessian commander, Colonel Rahl, steps into the middle of the room. The people grow quiet as he begins to speak.*)

RAHL: Ladies and gentlemen! I am glad to see that all of you are enjoying yourselves. I am especially happy to see so many Americans here.

FIRST MAN: (*Smiles*) It shows that some of us Americans are wise enough to remain friends of his Majesty, King George.

RAHL: (*Smiles*) I am a Hessian, sir. King George pays me well to be his friend.

FIRST OFFICER: You Americans should be glad you're not on the opposite side of the river with your General Washington. There are no Christmas parties in his army, I'm sure.

FIRST WOMAN: We hear the American army is very short on food.

SECOND MAN: I can't say I'm sorry!

SECOND WOMAN: Some of their soldiers came to our farm to buy food, but we refused to sell to them. We'd rather sell to the British forces.

RAHL: (*Laughs*) General Washington may be an "old fox" when it comes to pulling his soldiers away from a fight with larger forces. But he's not a clever enough fox to get chickens for his men. (*The company laughs.*)

FIRST MAN: How true, Colonel Rahl! How true!

RAHL: Now, ladies and gentlemen, we will have some dancing. Choose your partners, gentlemen.

THIRD WOMAN: Dancing, Colonel Rahl? Where are your musicians?

RAHL: They're ready in the next room, madam. Take your places, ladies and gentlemen. Then I will signal the musicians to begin.

(The men and women take their places on the dance floor. Rahl walks among them, as if to see that each has a partner. During this business, a man enters through the door at the side of the room. He wears a long, dark coat and a hat pulled down over his forehead. The dancers take no notice of him. One of the officers goes to him quickly.)

FIRST OFFICER: *(Angry, but low)* What do you mean by breaking in on our party?

HAWKINS: I have an important message for Colonel Rahl, sir.

FIRST OFFICER: Who are you?

HAWKINS: George Hawkins, sir, from General Washington's headquarters.

FIRST OFFICER: Oh, I didn't recognize you at first.

HAWKINS: May I give this note to Colonel Rahl, sir? It's very important. (*He takes a note out of his pocket.*) I must get back to camp before I'm missed. May I see Colonel Rahl, sir?

FIRST OFFICER: Colonel Rahl is very busy just now. Give me the note. I'll see that he gets it. (*He takes the note.*)

HAWKINS: At once, if you please, sir! I must rush back. (*He leaves quickly. At this moment Colonel Rahl turns and sees Hawkins leaving.*)

RAHL: Who was that?

FIRST OFFICER: That was Hawkins, sir, the spy we placed as General Washington's orderly. He brought this note for you.

RAHL: (*Takes the note and puts it into his pocket.*) I'll look at it tomorrow.

FIRST OFFICER: But Hawkins said it was very important, Colonel Rahl.

RAHL: Nothing can be so important on Christmas Day. The note can wait till tomorrow morning. There's a lady over at the back who needs a partner for the dance. Go over there. (*He claps his hands and raises his voice.*) Musicians! Music for the dance.
 (*The music starts off stage. The company dances. When the dance is finished, Colonel Rahl speaks up again.*)

RAHL: Bravo! That was fine! Now, ladies and gentlemen, what do you say to a different dance?

VOICES: Fine! Yes, another! Let's dance again!
 (*Music starts again. Dancing continues as curtain is drawn.*)

SCENE 4

Time: The next morning
Place: Colonel Rahl's headquarters

RAHL: (*Stretching*) Oh, but it's hard to get up early after such a fine Christmas party.

FIRST OFFICER: Yes, it was a fine party, sir. But, Colonel Rahl, have you read that note I gave you last night?

RAHL: Note? What note?

FIRST OFFICER: The note that Hawkins, our spy, brought to the party. I gave it to you just as the dancing was about to begin.

RAHL: (*Searches his pockets*) Oh, yes. Let's see, what did I do with it?

(*Gunfire is heard off stage.*)

FIRST OFFICER: (*Startled*) What was that?

RAHL: It sounds like gunfire. What can it mean?

SECOND OFFICER: (*Rushing into the room*) The Americans! The Americans are here! They are attacking! The town is full of them!

(*More gunfire, closer this time*)

RAHL: The Americans! To your places! Rouse the men! That old fox Washington has tricked us again!

(*The guns boom as all rush off the stage.*)

CURTAIN

Time: April 30, 1789
Place: A street in New York

(*People are hurrying along in one direction. Tommy and Uncle Joe walk in slowly.*)

82

TOMMY: That was a clever surprise trick General Washington played on the Hessians. He certainly caught them off guard! Do you think the Americans would have won the battle of Trenton, Uncle Joe, if the Hessian commander had read the spy's note right away?

UNCLE: Who can tell now, Tommy? That commander was killed in the battle. The note, still sealed, was found in his pocket.

(Cheering is heard off stage: "Long live General Washington!" "Hurray for General Washington!")

TOMMY: Listen! The people are cheering! General Washington must have arrived at Federal Hall! Let's hurry!

UNCLE: We just have to turn the corner, Tommy. In a few minutes General George Washington will become the first President of the United States.

(The cheering continues as Tommy and Uncle Joe walk quickly off the stage.)

THE END

Sacajawea

CAST

RED WOLF	BIG ELK
LEAPING FISH	WILLIAM CLARK
WHITE CLOUD	MERIWETHER LEWIS
SACAJAWEA	GEORGE
BRIGHT FEATHER	MANDAN CHIEF
TOUSSAINT CHARBONNEAU	CAM-EE-AH-WAIT

WHITE MEN, INDIAN WARRIORS

SCENE 1

Time: Afternoon of a day in October, 1804
Place: Camp of the Mandan Indians

(*A few tepees are seen among the trees in the background. Two boys who face one side of the stage are having a contest with bows and arrows. They bend their bows toward that side. In the center three women are sitting on tree stumps. Sacajawea is sewing on a pair of moccasins. White Cloud is shaping a clay jar with her fingers. Bright Feather holds a bowl filled with corn in her lap. As the curtain rises, one of the boys is taking careful aim with his bow. He lets his arrow fly.*)

85

RED WOLF: I win! My arrow hit right in the center of the pine tree.

LEAPING FISH: But my arrow hit the bird that was sitting on the branch of the tree. That was a better shot.

RED WOLF: But we were aiming at the center of the tree.

WHITE CLOUD: (*Scolding*) Red Wolf! Leaping Fish! Stop your quarreling! You can both hit your mark with the arrow.

SACAJAWEA: Run to the edge of the clearing, both of you, and see if you can spy the hunters who went out for buffalo two suns ago. Then you can be the first to bring us the news of their coming. (*The boys run off.*)

BRIGHT FEATHER: If the men don't come home with buffalo meat today, I shall have to pound this corn into meal. I was hoping I could cook the corn with the meat.

WHITE CLOUD: That's a pretty design you're sewing on the toe of your moccasin, Sacajawea. It's not a design of our Mandan tribe.

BRIGHT FEATHER: Is it a design of the Minnetaree tribe, where you came from, Sacajawea?

SACAJAWEA: No, Bright Feather. It's a design I learned when I was a child among my own people, the Shoshones.

WHITE CLOUD: The Shoshones! You have lived among us Mandans many, many moons. Yet you still call yourself a Shoshone.[1]

BRIGHT FEATHER: You are the squaw of Toussaint Charbonneau. Although his father was French, his mother was a Mandan. Why don't you forget the Shoshones, and call yourself a Mandan?

SACAJAWEA: I can never forget my own people. How can you ask me to forget my parents, my brother, the friends I played with when I was a child? My heart has been sick for them these many, many moons.

(*The boys run across the stage as they call out*)

RED WOLF: The hunters are back! The hunters are back!

LEAPING FISH: The hunters have brought buffalo meat! The hunters are back!

BRIGHT FEATHER: Good news! I must go and prepare this corn to cook with the meat.

WHITE CLOUD: And I must go and help cut up the share of meat for my family.

(*Bright Feather and White Cloud leave at one side as Charbonneau enters from the other side. Sacajawea rises as he comes in.*)

CHARBONNEAU: I'm back, Sacajawea. We found many buffalo. There will be much meat to dry for the winter.

SACAJAWEA: That's good news, Toussaint. Perhaps — perhaps you have even better news for me.

CHARBONNEAU: (*Surprised*) What can be better news than that we shall have enough food for the winter ahead?

[1] Shoh·sho'·nee

SACAJAWEA: While you were out hunting, Toussaint, did you meet any of my people?

CHARBONNEAU: No, I didn't see any Shoshones. You ask that every time I return from a long hunt. You ask that of every hunter or trader who comes to our camp.

SACAJAWEA: When my brother, Sagawa,[1] and I were captured by the Minnetarees, we made a promise to each other. We promised that if we were ever separated, we would always hunt for each other.

CHARBONNEAU: You were just children when the Minnetarees captured you. It is many, many moons since I bought you from the Minnetarees. Can't you forget that you were once a Shoshone?

SACAJAWEA: I have never given up hope that some day I shall once again see my people.

(*Red Wolf and Leaping Fish run in. They stop before Sacajawea and Charbonneau.*)

RED WOLF: (*Somewhat breathless*) The white men have come!

LEAPING FISH: Many white men!

RED WOLF: They came in a large boat!

LEAPING FISH: The boat has a big white wing on it!

RED WOLF: And there are smaller boats, too. The small boats have white wings, too!

CHARBONNEAU: (*Smiles, puts a hand on their shoulders*) Stop and catch your breath, Red Wolf, and you, too, Leaping Fish. We have all seen white men before. The important thing is, how do they look? Do they look angry or friendly?

LEAPING FISH: They smile when they talk to our men.

(*Big Elk, a warrior, enters.*)

[1] Sah·gah′·wah

BIG ELK: Charbonneau! Two white chiefs are here from the land where the sun rises. They say they want to talk to you and your squaw.

CHARBONNEAU: Two white chiefs, Big Elk? Are they fur traders?

BIG ELK: I don't think so. They didn't talk about furs.

CARBONNEAU: What do they want of me?

BIG ELK: They did not say. The white men are building a lodge to live in for the winter. In a few days, the white chiefs say, they will ask our chief and you and your squaw to visit them in their lodge.

SACAJAWEA: The white chiefs have many boats. They must be big chiefs and have much power in their own lands. We must listen to what they say, Toussaint.

CHARBONNEAU: If they are not a war party, I wonder why they came in so many boats? I wonder what they want of you and me, Sacajawea?

SCENE 2

Time: A few days later

Place: A clearing outside the camp of Captain Meriwether Lewis and Captain William Clark. Wooden huts in background.

(*Lewis is sitting on a tree stump, writing in a notebook, as Clark enters.*)

CLARK: Well, Merry, what are you putting down in your notebook now?

LEWIS: A few more notes about the animals we found on the last part of our journey, Bill.

CLARK: That last grizzly bear was a fierce one, all right! It took three shots to finish him off.

LEWIS: The grizzlies have been our worst enemies. That is, aside from the mosquitoes that bothered us so much. Unfortunately we couldn't shoot them!

CLARK: You're forgetting some of the Indians, Merry. Some of those tribes were mighty troublesome, until we showed them we were a match for them.

LEWIS: We had to show them we wouldn't stand for any trouble from them. I hope this Mandan tribe will be friendly and helpful. (*Smiles*) By the way, Bill, do you know what these Indians have named us?

CLARK: No. What?

LEWIS: They call you Red Hair.

CLARK: It's not hard to guess why. (*He rubs his head.*) And what do they call you? I'm sure no Indian would call you Captain Meriwether Lewis.

LEWIS: (*Puts his hand on the long knife at his belt*) They've noticed this long knife I always wear at my belt, so they've nicknamed me Long Knife.

(*Enter George, quickly.*)

GEORGE: Captain Lewis! Captain Clark!

CLARK: What is it, George?

GEORGE: We've just sighted the Indians coming up the path from the river.

CLARK: Good! Tell our men to stand around behind Captain Lewis and me, but to keep their guns out of sight.

GEORGE: You mean, sort of like a welcome committee, sir, only to keep their eyes open.

CLARK: To be on guard. That's right! Now, go, George. (*George leaves. The chief of the Mandans enters, followed by Charbonneau, Sacajawea, and several warriors. While the warriors are slowly grouping themselves in a half circle on each side of their chief, a number of white men enter and take their places at the back. Sacajawea keeps her eyes on the ground except when she is spoken to or must speak.*)

91

LEWIS: Welcome, Chief of the Mandan people! I am Captain Lewis, and this white chief is Captain Clark.

CHIEF: Welcome! My people call you Long Knife and Red Hair.

CHARBONNEAU: I am Charbonneau. This is my wife, Sacajawea. Her name means Bird Woman.

CLARK: Tell your wife, Charbonneau, that we feel it an honor for her to visit us.

SACAJAWEA: It is an honor for me to be here, Captain.

CLARK: (*Surprised*) What? Your wife speaks English, Charbonneau?

CHARBONNEAU: (*Proud*) Sacajawea speaks many languages. We learned English from the fur traders. I have taught her French, the language of my father. Sacajawea also speaks the languages of many Indian tribes.

LEWIS: This is better than we had hoped for! But we'll speak with you and your wife a little later, Charbonneau. We wish to speak to the Mandan chief first. (*Turns to the chief*) We have come from the Great White Chief in the East, the President of the United States. All this land from the Mississippi River, the Father of Waters, to the ocean in the far West now belongs to the United States of America. It no longer belongs to the Spanish people or the French people.

CLARK: Do you understand, Chief? The President of the United States is now your friend and protector. In turn, you must show yourselves friends of the Americans.

CHIEF: We will be friends with Americans if Americans be friends with us.

CLARK: We want your friendship. You can trust us.

CHIEF: Why are you here, so far from the home of the Great White Chief?

LEWIS: The Great White Chief has sent us to explore the land that now belongs to us, the land between the Mississippi River and the big sea far to the west.

CLARK: The Great White Chief has sent us to learn what rivers and mountains are in this land, what plants grow there, what animals live there. Most of all, he wants to find out the best places to set up trading posts with the Indians.

CHIEF: You cannot go to the big sea in the West in your boats, Red Hair.

CHARBONNEAU: The chief is right, Captain Clark. When you come to the big mountains, the Rocky Mountains, you will need horses. You will have to get horses from the Indians who live in that country.

CLARK: We have thought of that, Charbonneau. It is the country of the Shoshones. That is why we wanted to talk to you and your wife. We've heard that she speaks the Shoshone language.

LEWIS: Will you two come with us? Will you, Charbonneau, act as our guide, and let Sacajawea help us talk to the Shoshones?

SACAJAWEA: (*Looking eagerly at Charbonneau*) Say yes, Toussaint!

CHARBONNEAU: Sacajawea could guide you better than I can. She knows the country. She was born and brought up among the Shoshones.

SACAJAWEA: (*Eagerly, to Clark*) I can guide you to the land of the Shoshones! I remember every trail, every river, every tall rock, every mountain pass between this land and the land of my people!

LEWIS: We want your help, Sacajawea, but we also want to be fair to you. You are a woman. It will be a hard, rough journey. Are you sure you want to go with us?

SACAJAWEA: I am strong. l can paddle a canoe. I can carry a heavy pack. I can cook and make clothes. You will find me helpful.

CHARBONNEAU: (*Firm*) If you don't take Sacajawea, you can't have Charbonneau! No, sir!

CLARK: (*Smiles*) That seems to settle that! We're happy to have you both.

SACAJAWEA: One thing you must tell me before I promise, Red Hair. You must tell me that you mean no harm to my people, the Shoshones.

CLARK: We mean no harm to the Shoshones, Sacajawea, or to any other Indian tribe. We wish only to explore the land for the great White Chief.

SACAJAWEA: You speak good words. I guide you to the land of my people. (*Joyful, to Charbonneau*) Toussaint! I have prayed to the Great Spirit to help me find my people. Now perhaps I shall find them! Perhaps I can find my brother, Sagawa, and my friends of long ago!

SCENE 3

Time: Spring of the following year
Place: A trail in mountain country

(*The stage is empty when the curtain goes up. Clark enters, carrying a large box. He sets it down on the ground and turns in the direction from which he entered.*)

CLARK: (*Calls*) Come on, men! Bring the boxes over here, where they'll be safe. Quick!
(*Lewis enters, followed by Charbonneau and several other white men. Each carries a heavy box, which he sets down.*)
LEWIS: Whew! That was a narrow escape for us, Bill! I was sure we'd all drown in the river this time!
CHARBONNEAU: That wind came up so suddenly, the boat went spinning all around.

LEWIS: Where's Sacajawea, Charbonneau?

CHARBONNEAU: Over there with little Baptiste.[1] She's hanging his cradle board on the tree.

LEWIS: That small son of yours has had an exciting life so far, Charbonneau. He is not yet four months old, and he has traveled many miles up the Missouri with us. Today he has been shipwrecked.

CHARBONNEAU: He is a fine strong baby, and Sacajawea takes good care of him.

CLARK: Now let's check over our boxes and see how much of our supplies we lost overboard before we righted the boat.

[1] Bap·teest′

LEWIS: (*Worried*) It's not food supplies I'm worried about most. It's our medicines and surveying instruments.

CLARK: And all the notes we've made!

(*The men start looking over the boxes.*)

LEWIS: Do any of you see the box with our medicines?

CHARBONNEAU: (*Turns over a box*) Is this it? No, this one holds goods to trade with the Indians.

CLARK: We're in a pretty fix, Merry, if we've lost our supplies of medicines.

LEWIS: We're in a worse fix, in my opinion, if we've lost our surveying instruments and our notes on everything we've seen and done during these past weeks. We could never remember all those notes and figures.

CHARBONNEAU: I'll call my wife. Sacajawea will know where to look. (*Calls*) Sacajawea!

LEWIS: (*Gloomy*) If they've not been washed overboard and lost.

SACAJAWEA: You want me?

CLARK: Sacajawea, have you seen the boxes with our instruments and our medicines and papers?

SACAJAWEA: Yes, Red Hair. They are safe. I fished them out of the river when the boat went over.

CLARK: (*Relieved*) Good for you! I might have known we could count on you in time of need.

LEWIS: I hope the papers aren't wet through.

SACAJAWEA: You tell me these instruments and papers must always be safe. I remember that wind storms come up suddenly in this country. So I sew up the instruments and medicines and papers in deerskin to keep them from getting wet. When boxes go into the river, I fish them out.

CLARK: Sacajawea, you're a lifesaver! Without our medicines the health of our whole party would be in danger, and we might not be able to push on.

LEWIS: And without our surveying instruments and our notes, all our work so far would have been for nothing. We would have to return to the President and say our mission has been a failure.

CHARBONNEAU: This is another time, Captain Lewis, when you should be glad I would not come without Sacajawea.

LEWIS: You're right, Charbonneau. She has guided us along the right way. She has cooked for us, shown us plants and roots we could eat, made shirts and moccasins for us, and helped paddle our canoes. And all this while she has taken care of the little Baptiste, too.

CLARK: We can never thank you enough, Sacajawea. After this wet adventure in the river, I wonder if you've had enough of this rough journey? Would you want to go back to the Mandan camp? We could spare some men to go back with you.

(George enters. His manner is excited.)

GEORGE: Captain Lewis! Captain Clark!

CLARK: Yes, George? Why are you so excited?

GEORGE: I've been exploring around here since we beached our boat. There's a great waterfall ten minutes' walk from here.

SACAJAWEA: *(Excited)* A great waterfall? It must be the great falls we passed when my brother and I were captured by the Minnetarees! I remember it well! You ask if I wish to go back now? No! We are near the home of the Shoshones, my own people. We must start looking for them now. Somewhere near here I shall find my brother, my friends, my own people!

SCENE 4

Time: Several weeks later
Place: A camp on the prairie, mountains in the near distance.

(The Lewis and Clark party is standing at ease, waiting for the Indians to arrive.)

LEWIS: It's most remarkable, Charbonneau, how your wife guided us to this land of the Shoshones. Not a single trail and not a single branch of a river that was wrong!

CHARBONNEAU: (*Proud*) My Sacajawea is a bright squaw! She was only a child when she was stolen from her people, yet you see how she remembered every turn of the trail, every tall rock, every twisting stream.

99

CLARK: I hope she can help us make friends with these Shoshones. They may not be her own tribe or relatives. We must trade with them for horses and food supplies, so that we can complete our mission to the Pacific.

(*The sound of Indian drums is heard off stage.*)

LEWIS: I hear the Indian drums. Where is Sacajawea? We'll need her in a few minutes.

CHARBONNEAU: (*Looks off stage*) She's talking to some of those women. I'll get her.

(*Charbonneau leaves. The tom-toms are louder now.*)

CLARK: Here come the Indians now. Their chief is a fine-looking fellow, isn't he?

LEWIS: He's pretty young to be chief. What's his name?

CLARK: Chief Cam-ee-ah-wait. We'll have to ask the Indians to dance for us till Sacajawea comes back.

(*The drums stop. Chief Cam-ee-ah-wait enters, followed by a group of Indians. They form a half circle around the chief.*)

LEWIS: Welcome, Chief Cam-ee-ah-wait!

(*Chief nods.*)

CLARK: White men want peace. (*He makes the motions of smoking a peace pipe.*) Will you dance the peace dance for us? (*He moves his hands up and down in dance motions.*)

(*Cam-ee-ah-wait nods. He motions to the men. The Indians do a short dance. When the dance is ended, they again form a half circle around chief.*)

CLARK: (*Looks around impatiently*) Where's Sacajawea? I'm not good at sign language.

LEWIS: Here she comes, Bill. She always arrives in time when we need her.

(*Sacajawea enters. She keeps her eyes on the ground.*)

CLARK: Sacajawea, talk to the chief for us. Tell him we wish to trade with him for food and horses. Tell him we need help to get to the Pacific, the big sea far to the west. Tell him we want a guide to show us the way through the mountain passes.

LEWIS: (*Impatient*) Come, woman! Look up at the chief! He won't bite you!

SACAJAWEA: Indian women must keep eyes down when men are in council. But I will speak now.

(*She looks up at the chief. With a start of surprise she walks closer and looks steadily at him. Suddenly she puts her finger on her lips and begins to sway from side to side. The chief now looks surprised, looks closely at Sacajawea. Then he, too, puts a finger on his lips and begins to sway from side to side.*)

CLARK: What is this? Some kind of Shoshone sign?

LEWIS: Have they both gone mad? What is this?

SACAJAWEA: (*Cries out joyfully*) Sagawa! My brother!

CHIEF: Sacajawea!

(*Sacajawea and Cam-ee-ah-wait put their hands on each other's shoulders for a few seconds. Then Sacajawea covers her eyes, as if crying for joy.*)

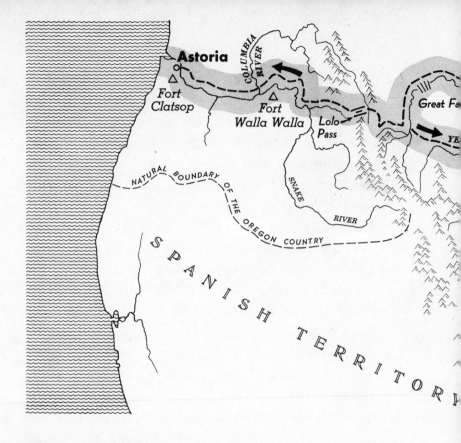

LEWIS: Sacajawea! You don't mean ——!

SACAJAWEA: (*Takes her hands off her face, smiles happily*) The Great Spirit has given me my wish! I have found my brother! This is Sagawa, my brother, now the chief of my people, now called Cam-ee-ah-wait, meaning Smoke and Thunder.

CLARK: But what did those signs mean — the finger on your lips, the swaying from side to side?

SACAJAWEA: When we were captured by the Minnetarees we made up these signs. If we ever met again after many moons, we would know each other by these signs.

CLARK: (*To Lewis*) Well, if this isn't the most surprising thing in the world, Merry!

LEWIS: The greatest piece of good luck for us, too, Bill.

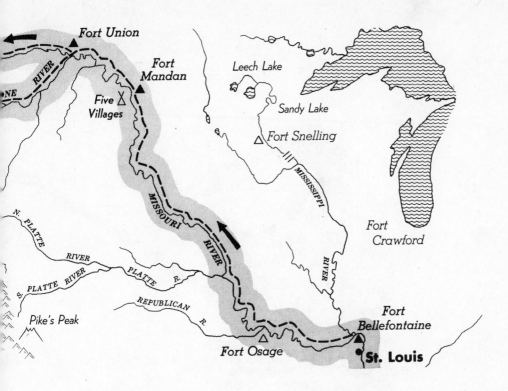

Sacajawea, will you ask Chief Cam-ee-ah-wait if he will trade us food and horses and give us a guide to the Pacific?

SACAJAWEA: He is my brother. He will give you what you need to get through the passes to the Pacific.

LEWIS: And what about you, Sacajawea? Now that you have found your brother and your own people, will you stay with them?

SACAJAWEA: No. I promised only that I would help my white brothers find their way to the land of the Shoshones. But my white brothers still need my help. I go with you all the way to the big sea in the far West. I help you carry out the mission of the Great White Chief, the President.

THE END

Sam

Houston

Brother of the Cherokees

CAST

JAMES HOUSTON	SOLDIER
JOHN HOUSTON	GENERAL JACKSON
SAM HOUSTON	FIRST CHIEF
CHIEF OO-LOO-TE-KA	BEN
MRS. HOUSTON	SECOND CHIEF
MARY HOUSTON	THIRD CHIEF

SCENE 1

Time: 1808
Place: A wooded spot on an island

(*John and James Houston enter. They stop part way across the stage and look around.*)

JAMES: This is the island where that trader said we'd find Sam. Where do you suppose we should start looking for him, John?

JOHN: My guess would be the lodges of the Cherokee Indians, James. You know, ever since our family moved to Tennessee, Sam has always slipped away to visit the Indians.

JAMES: We must find him. Ma's so worried about him.

JOHN: I don't know why Ma worries so about him. He's often disappeared into the woods for days at a time, and he's always come back safe.

JAMES: It's time he stopped that and settled down to a job for good. Which way is that Cherokee camp, do you suppose, John?

(*Sam Houston enters, whistling. He carries a book under his arm. He stops when he sees his brothers.*)

SAM: (*Mischievous smile*) Well, if it isn't my two big brothers! How did you get here?

JOHN: Never mind your silly questions, Sam! We've been looking for you, to fetch you home.

SAM: Why should I go back to the farm? I like it better here in the woods.

JOHN: (*Kind*) Sam, come back to your own family.

SAM: Tell Ma I'll be back to see her very soon. She mustn't worry about me. The Indians are my friends.

JOHN: But suppose these Indians should go on the warpath against the settlers here? What would you do then?

SAM: I'd try to talk them out of it if I could. But the Indians aren't always wrong, you know.

JAMES: (*Impatient*) Come on, John, It's no use talking to him.

(*He starts to leave. John follows slowly.*)

SAM: Give my love to Ma and my sisters. Tell them not to worry about me. I'll come home on a visit soon.

(*Sam watches his brothers leave. When they have disappeared, Chief Oo-loo-te-ka enters from the opposite side.*)

OO-LOO-TE-KA: Those two men — who are they, Sam?

SAM: My older brothers, Chief Oo-loo-te-ka.

OO-LOÒ-TE-KA: What do they want here?

SAM: They want me to go home.

OO-LOO-TE-KA: You are leaving us?

SAM: No. I told my brothers I'd rather stay here.

OO-LOO-TE-KA: You are a fine boy, Sam. You are like one of us in the lodge of the Cherokees. I shall make you my son, brother to all in my tribe.

SAM: (*Happy*) You mean, you will adopt me as your son, as one of your tribe?

OO-LOO-TE-KA: I shall adopt you as my son. You are still a boy, Sam. A boy needs a father.

SAM: You make me very proud, Chief Oo-loo-te-ka! To be adopted as your son is a great honor for me!

OO-LOO-TE-KA: Tonight I shall tell the council of braves. Tomorrow you shall be adopted as one of us.

SAM: And will you give me an Indian name, too?

OO-LOO-TE-KA: You shall be called Co-lon-neh. It is the bird called the raven by the white men. You shall be Co-lon-neh, the son of Oo-loo-te-ka, Chief of the Cherokee Nation.

SAM: (*Stands up proudly*) I am Co-lon-neh, the Raven, son of Chief Oo-loo-te-ka, and brother to the Cherokees! I shall call them my brothers all my life!

SCENE 2

Time: 1813

Place: Kitchen of the Houston home

(*Mrs. Houston and her daughter Mary are busy with bowls and pots at the kitchen table. John is working on a heavy leather harness strap.*)

JOHN: (*Examines the strap*) There! I think this harness strap will hold now. We can't afford to buy a new strap every time one breaks.

MRS. HOUSTON: No, we've still got to be careful how we spend cash. You boys have worked hard to make the farm and the store give us a good living, but we have to hold on to cash.

MARY: All of us children have worked hard, Ma, except Sam. He hasn't been much help.

JOHN: No, he'd still rather read a book under the trees or hunt with the Indians.

MARY: Since he was adopted into the Indian tribe, Sam'd rather be called by his Indian name than by the one you and Pa gave him.

MRS. HOUSTON: Well, we'll have to let Sam go his own way, Mary. People don't all take to the same things. When Sam came back home last year and decided to open a school, I thought he surely meant to settle down at last. But he's closed down the school.

MARY: I wonder where he is right now?

MRS. HOUSTON: When he left the house this morning, he said he was just going out to hunt. No telling when he'll be back, though. We won't wait supper for him. Go out to the pump and wash up, John.

(The door opens and Sam enters. He's dressed in Indian buckskins. He sets his musket against the wall.)

SAM: Hello, everybody! Shot a fine wild turkey this morning. It's out in the wood shed right now. Didn't want any feathers inside the house, Ma.

MRS. HOUSTON: That's good, Sam. We need some fresh meat right now. Supper's ready. I was just telling John to go out and wash up.

SAM: Ma, I've got something important to tell you. I'll be leaving tomorrow.

JOHN: Is that supposed to be surprising news to us?

MARY: Going back to your Cherokee friends for a change, Sam?

SAM: Not this time, Mary. I've just taken the Government's silver dollar off the drum.

MARY: What do you mean?

SAM: I've joined the United States Army. I'm off to fight the Creek Indians with General Jackson.

MRS. HOUSTON: Oh, Sam! Where will you be going?

SAM: To Alabama. The British have stirred up the Creek Indians there, and they are on the war path against us. General Jackson is marching down there to settle those Indians.

JOHN: So now you think you want to be a soldier!

SAM: It's the way I can serve my country when she needs me, John.

MRS. HOUSTON: Leave him alone, John. Sam, if you have a wish to serve your country as a soldier, I'm not going to stop you.

SAM: I knew you'd see it my way, Ma.

MRS. HOUSTON: I'll say only this to you, Sam. If you're going to be a soldier, be a brave soldier.

SAM: I'll try to be as brave a soldier as my father was.

MRS. HOUSTON: When you leave, take your father's musket with you. Never disgrace it! And take this, too. (*She takes a ring off her finger.*) This ring belonged to your father. Read the word inside.

SAM: (*Takes the ring and looks inside*) The word is *Honor*.

MRS. HOUSTON: (*Nods her head*) *Honor!* That's the word that must forever shine in your life, Sam!

SAM: (*Puts the ring on his finger*) *Honor!* It's a mighty fine word to live by, Ma. I'll try to live by it always!

SCENE 3

Time: Early 1818
Place: General Jackson's Headquarters

(*General Jackson is seated at a table, working at some papers. A soldier works at a smaller table near the door at one side of the room. There's a knock at the door. When the soldier opens it, Sam Houston stands in the doorway. He wears the uniform of an army lieutenant. The soldier salutes, and Lieutenant Houston returns the salute.*)

SOLDIER: Have you an appointment with General Jackson, sir?

HOUSTON: Lieutenant Houston, reporting to General Jackson, as ordered.

JACKSON: (*Looks up and smiles*) Oh! Come in, Lieutenant Houston. Come in! (*Houston walks over to Jackson's desk. The two men salute.*) Sit down. I wouldn't keep a wounded soldier standing. (*To the soldier*) Daniels, take your work somewhere else for a while, will you? I'll call you when I'm through talking to Lieutenant Houston.

SOLDIER: Very well, sir. (*He picks up his papers and leaves.*)

JACKSON: How do you feel, Houston? It's several years since we fought together. Are your wounds all healed?

HOUSTON: Not quite, sir. My arm has healed up fairly well, and the doctors removed the ball from my shoulder at last. But they tell me that the shoulder's likely to give me trouble the rest of my life.

JACKSON: Let's hope they're wrong. That battle of Horse-shoe Bend was no picnic for you. I noticed how bravely you led your men in the charge against the Creek Indians. You refused to move back, even when you were wounded. If I hadn't come along and *ordered* you back to have your wounds dressed, you might be fighting there yet.

HOUSTON: (*Smiles*) I don't think so, General. You whipped those Indians badly!

JACKSON: I remembered the way you set an example for your men that day, and I've been asking questions about you. I've found out, for one thing, that you spent some time living among the Cherokees.

HOUSTON: Then you probably know, sir, that Chief Oo-loo-te-ka adopted me as his son when I was about fifteen. He gave me the Indian name of Co-lon-neh, which means the Raven, as you may know.

JACKSON: I learned that, too, and I know that the Indians believe the Raven is a wise bird. That's why I've asked you to come here just now. I have an important task for you.

HOUSTON: I hope I can carry it out well enough to please you, General.

JACKSON: Let's hope so. As you may know, Lieutenant Houston, some chiefs of the Cherokee tribes signed a treaty with the United States Government two years ago. They gave us a large stretch of their lands in eastern Tennessee in exchange for land west of the Mississippi River. The treaty was supposed to be for the whole Cherokee nation.

HOUSTON: Chief Oo-loo-te-ka told me of this, sir, at the time he signed the treaty.

JACKSON: Well, it turns out now that some of the chiefs who didn't sign the treaty for their own tribe now refuse to leave their homes and move to the new land across the Mississippi. The chiefs who signed the treaty can't force them to leave. There are reports of trouble.

HOUSTON: Do you believe those Indians are ready to go on the warpath rather than give up their lands and move?

JACKSON: I'm afraid they may be planning a war. They say they weren't asked whether they wanted to sign the treaty. They say that as they didn't sign it, they can't be expected to obey it.

HOUSTON: That is bad, sir. I know some of those chiefs, and I know they're quick to look for trouble.

JACKSON: I'm anxious not to have an Indian war back here in Tennessee right now, Houston. You see, I'm about to march against the Seminole Indians on the border between Georgia and Florida. They've been burning our villages and killing the settlers down there.

HOUSTON: I can see why you wouldn't want another Indian war here, behind your back, General. But how can I help you? What's the task you have for me?

JACKSON: A very important one, Houston. I want you to act as peacemaker between the United States Government and the Cherokees. You've lived among them. You speak their language. You'll know how to talk to them and to keep them from going to war against the Government.

HOUSTON: That won't be an easy task, General Jackson, especially if those Indians feel that the Government hasn't treated them right. Have they any good reason for believing that?

JACKSON: Well, the Government promised them money and goods every year, in addition to the land on the other side of the river. It's possible that some Government agent hasn't been honest, and has been cheating the Indians.

HOUSTON: If some agent has been cheating them out of their rights, you can't blame the Indians for thinking the Government hasn't been fair to them. You can see why they'd be angry enough to go on the warpath. It will be hard to talk them out of it.

JACKSON: You've got to, Lieutenant Houston! I'm writing the Secretary of War to transfer you to the Indian country. As soon as the Secretary approves your transfer, you will go out and act as the Government agent to the Cherokees. They must be kept from making war on us, especially at this time! This is your task, Lieutenant Houston.

HOUSTON: You may depend on me to do my best, General Jackson. The Cherokee chief, Oo-loo-te-ka, calls me his son. The braves of his tribe call me their brother. I shall do my best to keep peace between them and our Government.

SCENE 4

Time: A few weeks later
Place: The Cherokee camp in a small clearing in the forest

(*Several Indian lodges can be seen against the forest background. Chief Oo-loo-te-ka stands under some trees with a group of chiefs of other tribes. One of these chiefs looks to one side and nods in that direction.*)

FIRST CHIEF: He comes. White brother Co-lon-neh comes. (*Houston enters, dressed in Indian buckskins. Behind him comes Ben, another white man, pushing a wheelbarrow covered with a cloth. They both stop in front of the group of Indians. Chief Oo-loo-te-ka nods his head slowly in greeting to Houston.*)

115

OO-LOO-TE-KA: Welcome, Co-lon-neh! Welcome back to the home of your father and brothers!

HOUSTON: (*Nods his head in greeting*) Co-lon-neh greets his father and his brothers. This is my friend and helper, Ben.

OO-LOO-TE-KA: My son's friend is welcome.

HOUSTON: Co-lon-neh comes to talk peace with his brothers.

SECOND CHIEF: There can be no peace between the white man and the Cherokees.

THIRD CHIEF: The Cherokee tribes are ready to beat the war drums.

HOUSTON: Why, my brothers, should you go to war with the United States Government? The Great White Father in Washington has kind feelings for you.

OO-LOO-TE-KA: The Great White Father has not kept his word. He does not give us what he promised. He cheats us.

HOUSTON: It is not the Great White Father in Washington or the Government that is cheating you. One of the agents has not been honest, and he will be punished. See what the Great White Father sends you now. (*He takes the cloth off the wheelbarrow.*)

BEN: Shall I take everything out at once, Lieutenant Houston?

HOUSTON: No, we'll take out one thing at a time, Ben.

BEN: Very well, sir.

(*Houston and Ben take out one thing at a time and hold it up as Houston talks about it, then lay it on the ground.*)

HOUSTON: Here's a bright new blanket for you, Chief Oo-loo-te-ka. It will keep your shoulders warm on the coldest day.

OO-LOO-TE-KA: Thank you, Co-lon-neh. You have thought of your father.

HOUSTON: There are more blankets for the other chiefs, and for all your braves, too, in the agent's station. Now, look at this cooking pot. We have many, many more like this one for the lodge fires of your squaws. The Great White Father also sends you many bows and arrows for the hunters in your tribe.

BEN: Excuse me, Lieutenant Houston. Don't forget the other gifts for the women.

HOUSTON: No, I won't forget those, Ben. See these chains of beads, and the bright ribbons, too, for the young braves and the squaws.

FIRST CHIEF: Our brother Co-lon-neh is good. He brings many fine gifts to his Cherokee brothers.

HOUSTON: These gifts are not from me, Chief. They are sent to you by the United States Government, by the Great White Father in Washington. He wishes the Cherokees well.

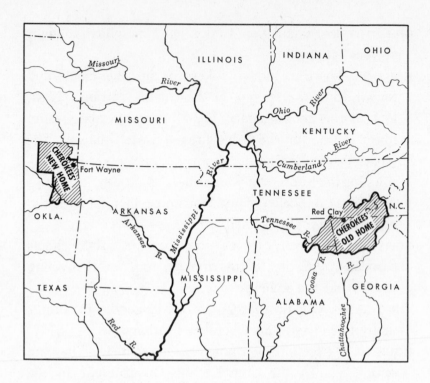

SECOND CHIEF: He does not show it by his acts. He made promises to the Cherokees, but he does not keep them. That is why we are ready to make war against him.

OO-LOO-TE-KA: The Great White Father wanted the lands of the Cherokees. He asked us to move our homes across the big river, the Father of Waters.

HOUSTON: Yes, but he gave you other land across the Mississippi as payment. Why won't you go west of the river?

OO-LOO-TE-KA: The other side of the Father of Waters is the land where the sun goes down, the Darkening Land. It is the land where danger and evil things live.

THIRD CHIEF: We live now in the east, the Sun Land. We don't like to turn our backs on the Sun Land.

FIRST CHIEF: We fear the danger and the evil things in the Darkening Land.

OO-LOO-TE-KA: You see now, Co-lon-neh, my son, brother of the Cherokees. This side of the river has always been our home. We have known only the Land of the Rising Sun. Our gods live in these mountains, in these corn-fields, in these forests. How can we move to the un-known land, the Land of the Darkening Sun, and leave our gods behind us?

HOUSTON: You will find your gods across the river, too, Chief Oo-loo-te-ka. Your gods will go with you into the mountains and the forests over there. They will protect you on the other side of the Father of Waters, just as they take care of you here.

SECOND CHIEF: My braves and I, we do not want to leave.

HOUSTON: But the Cherokees made a treaty, a paper talk, with the Government. Your chiefs signed the paper talk for all the tribes of the Cherokee nation. A paper talk must be kept. It is always the way of the Chero-kees to keep their word.

THIRD CHIEF: Not all the chiefs signed the paper talk. Some of us did not. Some of us were not asked whether we wanted to leave our homes and go to the Darkening Land. We who were not asked are angry because we must move.

OO-LOO-TE-KA: That is not the only reason some of our people are angry at the Great White Father in Washing-ton, Co-lon-neh. In the paper talk, he promised us food and money every year for giving up our lands here. It is two years now, and many of us have not received any food or money. Some of us have received only a little.

119

HOUSTON: The Great White Father in Washington is not to be blamed for this, Chief Oo-loo-te-ka. As I said before, it is the fault of a dishonest Government agent. He puts your money into his pocket. He is cheating you, and cheating the Government, too.

OO-LOO-TE-KA: Why does the Great White Father allow this?

HOUSTON: He didn't know of this before. Now the Great White Father has made me your agent, to watch over you and pay you what our paper talk promised.

OO-LOO-TE-KA: You are now the Government agent, Co-lon-neh?

HOUSTON: Yes, my father. I, Co-lon-neh, tell all my Cherokee brothers that they will be well off on the other side of the Father of Waters, the Mississippi River. The paper talk promises you that the white man will never go to your new lands. He will stay away, and let you live in peace there.

OO-LOO-TE-KA: And we will get the money and the food, as the paper talk promised us?

HOUSTON: I, Co-lon-neh, your son, and brother to the Cherokees, give you my word that this shall be done, according to the treaty.

OO-LOO-TE-KA: We know that we can trust the word of Co-lon-neh. I do not like war. My name, Oo-loo-te-ka, means "He who puts the drum away." My tribe shall not go on the warpath. I shall lead my people across the Father of Waters.

FIRST CHIEF: I, too, trust the word of Co-lon-neh. I shall tell my people that Co-lon-neh says it is wise to leave our homes here.

SECOND CHIEF: I, too, shall take the word of Co-lon-neh.

THIRD CHIEF: My people shall go in peace because Co-lon-neh says so.

OO-LOO-TE-KA: Go back to the Great White Father in Washington, Co-lon-neh, my son. Tell him the Cherokees will not make war on him.

HOUSTON: Good! You are wise, as always, Chief Oo-loo-te-ka. The promises in the paper talk will be kept by both sides. The Great White Father will be glad to know that there will be no war between us.

THE END

Abraham

Lincoln

With Malice Toward None

CAST

MISS HALL   DODGE
CAPTAIN JOHN PECK   MR. CHITTENDEN
ANDREWS   ABRAHAM LINCOLN
CAREY   WILLIAM SCOTT
A SOLDIER

SCENE 1

Time: September, 1861
Place: Office of Mr. Chittenden

(*Miss Hall stands between Mr. Chittenden's desk and the door. Captain Peck and Privates Carey, Dodge, and Andrews are near the door.*)

MISS HALL: I'm sorry, Captain, but Mr. Chittenden sees no one without an appointment.

PECK: But this is terribly important, Miss! There wasn't time to make an appointment.

MISS HALL: Mr. Chittenden is a very busy man, as you must surely realize. Those of us who work in the Treasury Department are putting in long days right now. I might be able to make an appointment for you for some time next week, however.

CAREY: Next week! Oh, no, Miss! That's too late!

MISS HALL: Then I'm sorry, gentlemen. I'll have to ask you to leave.

PECK: But I tell you, it's terribly important for us to see him, Miss! It's a matter of life and death! We must see Mr. Chittenden!

(*Chittenden enters and walks to his desk.*)

CHITTENDEN: Good morning, Miss Hall. Have I an appointment with these gentlemen?

MISS HALL: Good morning, Mr. Chittenden. No, these soldiers are about to leave.

(*The soldiers talk fast, almost interrupting each other.*)

PECK: Please, Mr. Chittenden! We haven't an appointment, but we must talk to you!

ANDREWS: It's terribly important, sir!

DODGE: It's a matter of life and death, sir!

CAREY: You've got to help us, sir!

CHITTENDEN: If you will calm down, men, and let your Captain speak for you, perhaps I can find out what you want of me.

PECK: I'm Captain John Peck, sir. These boys and I, we're a committee from our regiment — Company K, third regiment of Vermont. We've come to you for help because we're all strangers in Washington.

CHITTENDEN: But why to me, Captain?

PECK: Because you're a Vermonter yourself, and we're nearly all Vermonters. It's one of our Vermont boys who's in terrible trouble. You must help him, sir!

CHITTENDEN: I'll do anything I can to help out another Vermonter. Miss Hall, I won't need you just now. (*Smiles*) You needn't sound any alarm outside. I'm safe with these Green Mountain boys.

MISS HALL: Very well, Mr. Chittenden. (*She takes some papers and leaves.*)

CHITTENDEN: Now, suppose you tell me the story.

PECK: Well, sir, it's about Will Scott. He enlisted only a couple of months ago. He's only eighteen, and his mother allowed him to enlist only because I promised to look after him.ˑ

CHITTENDEN: I see. We have many boys even younger than that who are eager to fight to save the Union. Go on, Captain. I suppose young Scott has gotten into trouble?

PECK: The worst kind of trouble, sir. Three nights ago he was on sentry duty. The soldier who was to relieve him found him fast asleep at his post.

CHITTENDEN: (*Shocked*) A sentry asleep at his post on
night duty! That's bad! A very serious thing! A crime!

PECK: We know it. We're all agreed it's a most serious
thing. Will Scott was court-martialed yesterday.

CHITTENDEN: He was found guilty, I'm sure. And what
was the sentence given him by the Army judges?

PECK: He was sentenced to be shot tomorrow morning.

CHITTENDEN: Don't you believe the sentence of the court-
martial is just? Suppose the enemy had attacked at the
point where Scott was on duty? Scott was fast asleep.
He couldn't have given our men any warning. Think
how many of our men might have died because he was
asleep.

PECK: I know, sir. But — it seems a strange thing to say
— but there was a good reason why Will Scott fell
asleep. The judges should have taken that into account, and not been so hard on him.

CHITTENDEN: What good excuse can there possibly be for a soldier who falls asleep on night sentry duty?

PECK: You see, the night before that, Will had volunteered to stand sentry guard in place of a sick man in our company. Will stayed awake all that night. The next night it was Will's own turn to stand sentry duty.

ANDREWS: And that, sir, means he had to stay awake two nights in a row, with hard drill during the day between.

DODGE: It's hard enough to stay awake one night, after drilling all day. When you've had no sleep the night before, either — well, you can see how dead tired poor Will was.

CAREY: You can see why the boy couldn't stay awake the second night. It's not fair to punish him by — by shooting him!

CHITTENDEN: That's the punishment for being asleep on sentry post. Scott is guilty.

PECK: But the court-martial judges should have taken into account the fact that he was not fit to be put on guard duty! He had stood guard for another man the night before! Oh, it's all my fault! If any one should be shot, I'm the one!

CHITTENDEN: Why do you blame yourself, Captain Peck?

PECK: I should have put some one else on duty in Will's place that night or taken his place myself.

ANDREWS: You know Will wouldn't have let you do that, Captain!

PECK: I promised his mother I'd watch out for him. If he's shot, everybody at home will say I'm the guilty one, and they'll be right!

CAREY: He's as fine a boy as you'll find in the army, Mr. Chittenden! He's not lazy or a coward!

DODGE: He's a young, healthy country boy, accustomed to sound, regular sleep, and he's been in the army only a couple of months.

PECK: You're a lawyer, sir. Can't you think of some way to save him? All the men in our company got together and offered all the money they have to try to get him off.

ANDREWS: We're even willing to sell our farms and use the money to help save Will Scott's life.

CHITTENDEN: Boys, I'm very much touched by your feelings towards Scott, and by your wish to stick by him. I'm proud of every one of you. Scott is in a desperate position. I can't see any way in which I can help him.

PECK: Oh, don't say that! You live in Washington. You're an important person here. You must know some one of importance on whom we can call for help — some one who has the power to get a pardon for Will Scott!

CHITTENDEN: There's only one man on earth who can save your young friend. (*Stands up suddenly*) Yes, I'll take you to him! Come with me, quickly, while I have the courage to ask a pardon for a sentry asleep at his post!

SCENE 2

Time: A few minutes later
Place: Private office of President Lincoln

(*President Lincoln is writing at his desk. There is a knock at his door. Before he can speak, the door is opened. Mr. Chittenden and the soldiers enter.*)

CHITTENDEN: I beg your pardon, Mr. Lincoln, for bursting in like this. May I speak to you on a matter of the greatest importance?

LINCOLN: (*Smiles*) I can't ask you and your friends to come in, Mr. Chittenden. It appears that you are already in. What can I do for you?

CHITTENDEN: Mr. President, I'll come straight to the point. These soldiers are Green Mountain men from my own state of Vermont. They don't want anything for themselves. They want something for a young private in their company. It's something you alone can give them.

LINCOLN: And what's that?

CHITTENDEN: The young man's life.

LINCOLN: His life?

CHITTENDEN: He's been court-martialed and sentenced to be shot tomorrow morning. These men are here to beg you to pardon him.

LINCOLN: He must be guilty of something mighty serious. Has he refused to obey orders in battle? Has he murdered some one?

CHITTENDEN: Tell your story to the President, Captain Peck.

PECK: (*Stammers*) I — I can't do it — very well. I'm not used to — talking to a man like — the President of the United States.

CHITTENDEN: Captain Peck, your friend's life depends on you. You must tell your story yourself. I know it only secondhand, as you men told it to me.

PECK: I'll try. It's — it's Will Scott, Mr. President. He's a boy of eighteen, from our town. Nearly our whole company's from that part of the Green Mountains.

LINCOLN: There are some fine people in that part of our country.

PECK: Will Scott is one of the finest boys anywhere in our country, Mr. President. But I must tell you his story. The night before last he was found asleep at his sentry post. Yesterday he was court-martialed and sentenced to be shot. He's — he's to be shot tomorrow morning.

LINCOLN: Asleep at his guard post! That's a very serious matter!

PECK: We all agree on that, Mr. President. But he couldn't help it! He wasn't to blame for falling asleep!

LINCOLN: No? Who else is to blame for his falling asleep?

PECK: I am, sir! I feel it was my fault. Will Scott had volunteered to stand guard for a sick man in our company the night before. Then, when it was his own turn, the next night, it was impossible for him to stay awake all night. I should have known that. I should have ordered some one else to stand guard in his place. I'm the guilty one!

LINCOLN: You should not feel guilty, Captain.

PECK: They mustn't shoot him like a traitor or a coward! Will's as brave and loyal a boy as can be found anywhere!

130

ANDREWS: As our company sees it, Mr. President, Will wasn't given a fair trial.

LINCOLN: Do you mean that General Smith and the other officers at the courtmartial weren't fair?

ANDREWS: It doesn't seem fair to us, Mr. President. They asked Will what he had to say for himself. He told the officers that he had never stayed up all night in his whole life before. He said that he had tried desperately to keep awake, but after drilling hard all day the second night was too much for him.

CAREY: He told them that at first he had thought of paying one of the other men to stand guard in his place. But he thought they might believe he was afraid to stand guard, and he decided to take a chance on being able to stay awake. Would you call him a coward, Mr. President?

LINCOLN: No, I wouldn't say he was a coward. Still — going to sleep on night guard duty!

DODGE: He didn't mean to fall asleep. He said that twice he fell asleep and woke himself up while he was marching up and down. Then — well, the next thing he knew, the guard who was to relieve him was shaking him awake.

ANDREWS: He wanted to be a good soldier, Mr. President. Will tried very hard to be a good soldier!

CAREY: He's only a young country boy, Mr. President. He got into this trouble only because he had helped out a sick comrade. They mustn't shoot him!

PECK: Will Scott's not a coward or a traitor, Mr. President! Do you believe a boy like Will ought to be shot like a dog?

LINCOLN: No, I don't!

PECK: Then you *will* help him, Mr. Lincoln? You *will* do something to save him from being shot tomorrow?

LINCOLN: You boys are mighty fine lawyers for your young comrade. But what can I do? (*To Chittenden*) What do you suggest that I do, Mr. Chittenden?

CHITTENDEN: I haven't had time to give your side of the matter any thought, Mr. Lincoln. I was so moved by the story as told by these wonderful friends of young Scott, that the only thing I thought of was to rush directly to you. Couldn't you sign an order to hold off the shooting until Scott's case can be examined more fully?

LINCOLN: No, I don't believe that will work. You don't know those army officers. They will believe that young Scott must be shot as an example to the other soldiers.

CHITTENDEN: But you don't agree with them, do you?

LINCOLN: I might agree with them if he were a deserter, or guilty of murder or some other great crime. But I don't believe that an honest, brave soldier, guilty of nothing except falling asleep because he did the work of two men, ought to be shot.

CHITTENDEN: (*Smiles*) The army officers always say you are too soft-hearted, Mr. President.

LINCOLN: I know they say it. But there are enough mothers and wives and sisters already made sad by war without adding to the number.

PECK: Then you will pardon Will Scott, Mr. President?

LINCOLN: As Commander in Chief of the Army and Navy, I believe I can do something for him. Captain, your young friend shall not be shot until I know more about his case.

MEN: Thank you, Mr. President! Thank you!

LINCOLN: Mr. Chittenden, I shall look into this case myself. I shall go up to that camp today. Then I shall be sure that no mistake will be made.

CHITTENDEN: That's a great load to put on your shoulders, Mr. President. It's really asking too much of the President of the United States to interest himself in the life of one private soldier.

LINCOLN: Young Scott's life is as valuable to him as a General's life is to the General. Boys, go back to your regiment. Will Scott won't be shot — at least not tomorrow!

SCENE 3

Time: Several hours later
Place: A small bare room

(*The room is furnished with only a cot against one wall. High above the cot is a narrow slit of a window. Will Scott sits on the cot, elbows on knees, head in his hands. The door is opened by a soldier.*)

SOLDIER: Stand up, Scott!
     (*Scott stands up as Lincoln enters.*)
Shall I stay in here with you, Mr. President?
LINCOLN: No, thank you. I'll call you when I'm ready to leave.
SOLDIER: Yes, sir! (*He salutes and goes out, shutting the door.*)

134

LINCOLN: Sit down, my boy. (*They both sit down on the cot.*)

SCOTT: (*Stammers with surprise and fear*) You're — you're President Lincoln!

LINCOLN: Yes. Don't look so frightened. Surely my face isn't ugly enough to scare a soldier!

SCOTT: I — I recognized you at once, sir. My father gave me a medal with your picture on it, and I always carry it with me. (*He takes a medal out of his pocket.*) It's one of those made when you were running for President. My father voted for you.

LINCOLN: Then I owe my job partly to your father. I'd like to thank him. Tell me, is your mother still living?

SCOTT: Yes, sir. She's the best mother that ever lived!

LINCOLN: I suppose you carry a photograph of her?

SCOTT: Oh, yes. (*Takes a small photo out of his pocket and hands it to Lincoln*) It's not a very good likeness. You can't see how sweet and lovely she is.

LINCOLN: (*Looks at photo and hands it back*) You love your mother, don't you, Scott?

SCOTT: With all my heart! (*Bursts out, almost in tears*) Why are you here, Mr. Lincoln? Why are you asking me about my mother? You know I'm to be shot tomorrow for sleeping at my sentry post. Isn't that hard enough to bear? Are you going to tell me that I've brought disgrace on my mother? I don't feel I've been a coward or a traitor by falling asleep. I couldn't help it, I tell you! I couldn't help it! (*He puts his arm across his face.*)

LINCOLN: I haven't come here to call you a disgrace to your parents and your country. The court-martial officers probably said plenty about that.

135

SCOTT: (*Takes his arm down*) They did, Mr. President, though I told them that I wanted to be a good soldier, that I had tried hard to be a good soldier. They can shoot me, and maybe it's right that they should. But I couldn't have tried harder to stay awake. I just couldn't do it.

LINCOLN: I'm sure you tried, at any rate.

SCOTT: May I ask you one last favor, Mr. President? It — it won't mean any trouble for you or any one else.

LINCOLN: What is it?

SCOTT: (*Shaky voice*) Could you fix it, sir, so that the firing party will be from another company, not my own? That's the hardest thing for me to bear — the thought that I'll be shot by my own comrades. (*He covers his eyes.*)

LINCOLN: (*Gently*) Stand up, my boy. (*They both stand. Lincoln puts a hand on Scott's shoulder.*) Look at me! (*Slight pause*) My boy, I believe you when you say that it was impossible for you to stay awake. I know that it happened partly because you helped out a sick comrade, not because you were careless. Will Scott, you are not going to be shot tomorrow.

SCOTT: (*Hardly believing it*) I'm — I'm not to be shot? Even though I fell asleep at my post?

LINCOLN: No. I believe you want to be a good soldier. You're too fine a boy to be shot like a traitor. I'm going to pardon you and send you back to your company.

SCOTT: Back to my company! (*Shaky with relief*) Oh, I can't believe it! I was expecting to die, and — and you're sending me back to my company! I can't speak! I can't thank you properly. I can't find the right words!

LINCOLN: Scott, I've gone to a lot of trouble on your account. I've come down from Washington for your sake, when I'm a very busy man. Now, how are you going to pay me?

SCOTT: Pay you, Mr. Lincoln? Why, I haven't thought of that yet. Here I was, expecting to die, and — and everything's changed in a minute.

LINCOLN: I've given you back your life.

SCOTT: I'm terribly grateful, as grateful as a man can ever be. But — it's all so sudden! I'm sure I can find a way to pay you, sir. I have a few dollars in the bank, and I'm sure my parents won't mind selling part of our farm, and maybe some of the boys in my company will lend me some money. I'm sure I can find a way to pay you.

LINCOLN: My boy, my bill is a very large one. Not all the money your parents can get for their entire farm, not all the money all your comrades can gather together, can pay my bill.

SCOTT: That sounds mighty hopeless. Then how ——?

LINCOLN: There's only one man in the whole world who can pay my bill. That's William Scott! If, from this day on, you always do your duty, and if, at the end of the war you can look at me and honestly say, "Sir, I have kept my promise and done my duty as a soldier," then my bill will be paid. Will Scott, will you make this promise and try to keep it?

SCOTT: I promise you, Mr. President, that I'll try to do my duty as a man and as a soldier. You will never regret giving me back my life!

LINCOLN: I hope I never shall, my boy! One minute from now you will be free again. You can begin keeping your promise right now. (*Smiles*) Salute your Commander in Chief! (*Scott salutes. Lincoln returns the salute and leaves. Scott stands at salute a few seconds longer.*)

SCOTT: (*Softly*) I'm pardoned! Heaven help me keep my promise to you, Mr. Lincoln!

THE END

138

Thomas

Jefferson Memorial in Washington

Jefferson

Defender of Liberty

CAST

NARRATOR	NANCY
MRS. GOWER	PATRICK HENRY
THOMAS JEFFERSON	JOHN RANDOLPH
JOHN BRIDGES	MRS. GRAAF
EDWARD SANDERS	JOHN ADAMS
MR. GOWER	BENJAMIN FRANKLIN
MARTHA JEFFERSON	ROGER SHERMAN
SUE POTTER	ROBERT LIVINGSTON

NARRATOR: In our own country, and in every other country in the world, the name of Thomas Jefferson stands for equal rights for all. Jefferson believed that all men, rich and poor alike, should have an equal right to life, liberty and happiness. All his life he worked for the right of each man to worship as he pleases, the right of each child to have a good education, and the right of all Americans to be free.

Jefferson was a young lawyer of twenty-six when he began his service to the people of his own colony, Virginia. It was in 1769 that he decided he could work best for his ideas if he were a member of the Virginia House of Burgesses. So he ran for election. In those days it was thought polite, and necessary, for a candidate to visit each voter personally and ask for his vote. No man would vote for a candidate who had been so impolite as not to visit him and ask him. So Thomas Jefferson made the rounds of his county on horseback.

SCENE 1

Time: Spring, 1769
Place: Outside the Red Lion Inn

(*A long table and several chairs stand under the trees in the yard of the Red Lion Inn. Above the front door hangs a sign with the name of the inn. Mrs. Gower is busy wiping the table and straightening the chairs. At the sound of a horse's hoofs coming to a stop off stage, she looks to the side.*)

MRS. GOWER: (*As if greeting some one she knows*) Oh, good morning, sir! I'll get the boy to take your horse to the barn. Come right in, Mr. Jefferson.

JEFFERSON: (*Comes on stage*) Good morning, Mrs. Gower. Don't bother about my horse. I can't stay long. How are you, and how is your husband?

MRS. GOWER: We're both well, thank you, sir. Will isn't here just now. He's taken a wagonload of vegetables to town. But I expect him home any minute now.

JEFFERSON: Then I'll wait a while.

MRS. GOWER: Will's always glad to see you, Mr. Jefferson, whenever you stop by on your rides. Will says you always treat him like a gentleman and your equal, even though he's only a poor innkeeper.

JEFFERSON: And why not? It just happens that I had a rich father. Right now I have a favor to ask of Will. You've probably seen by the papers that I'm running for election to the House of Burgesses.

MRS. GOWER: Are you, now, Mr. Jefferson! We don't get the papers. Will and I can't read, you see. But Will has the right to vote. He owns a house and enough land to have the right to vote.

(*Bridges and Sanders enter. They walk toward the table.*)

BRIDGES: (*Nods to Jefferson and Mrs. Gower*) By your leave, sir, ma'am. May we sit down?

MRS. GOWER: Certainly, gentlemen! A lovely day, isn't it? What can I do for you, gentlemen? (*Bridges and Sanders sit down at the table.*) Something cool to drink on this warm spring day, or is it a bite to eat you'd like?

SANDERS: We left our farms early, so we're ready for a mid-day dinner.

MRS. GOWER: It's not quite ready, gentlemen. I'll go into the kitchen and see if I can hurry things up. (*She leaves through the front door of the inn.*)

JEFFERSON: Excuse me, sirs. May I join you at the table? I'm Thomas Jefferson.

BRIDGES: Oh, Jefferson! You're running for the House of Burgesses, aren't you?

JEFFERSON: Yes. Do you live in this county? If you do, I'd like to talk to you, and ask you to give me your vote.

SANDERS: Yes, we both live in this county. I'm Edward Sanders, and this is John Bridges. He owns the farm next to mine.

BRIDGES: I've heard of you and some of your ideas, Mr. Jefferson. Some I like, and some I don't.

JEFFERSON: Well, let's talk things over, right here, gentlemen.

BRIDGES: They tell me you're for freedom of religion for every one.

JEFFERSON: That's right, sir. I believe a man should have the right to worship as he pleases. His religion should make no difference, as long as he's a good man.

BRIDGES: Good! I came here from England because I don't hold the beliefs of the Church of England.

SANDERS: And I came to America from Germany because I wanted to worship according to my own belief.

JEFFERSON: A great many people came to America for religious freedom, and the colonies are the better for them.

BRIDGES: We're allowed to worship in our own church, here in Virginia, without being arrested and put into prison. But to my mind, we don't really have religious freedom here. The Church of England is the State religion of Virginia. That's not my religion, yet I have to pay a yearly tax to support that church.

SANDERS: Mr. Jefferson, do you believe people should have to pay a tax to support a church of a religion they don't believe in?

JEFFERSON: No, gentlemen! I certainly do not! I believe in real freedom of religion. No one should be asked to support a church in which he doesn't believe.

BRIDGES: You really mean that?

JEFFERSON: I do! If I'm elected to the House of Burgesses, I will work to have the church tax dropped.

SANDERS: Then you have my vote, Mr. Jefferson.

BRIDGES: I'm glad to hear you say that, Mr. Jefferson. Now, there's another idea of yours that I'm not so sure is a good one.

JEFFERSON: What's that? Let's talk it over, Mr. Bridges.

BRIDGES: You've been saying that every person should have an education. Now, I don't think it's necessary for everyone to know how to read and write. It's all right if he owns a lot of property, or he has money enough to study law or medicine.

145

JEFFERSON: (*Firm*) I believe every person has a right to an education, and should have it. What's more, I believe that the Government should set up schools so that every child can get an education, whether his parents have money or not.

SANDERS: You mean, the Government should set up free schools?

JEFFERSON: Exactly I'm for free public schools.

BRIDGES: (*Shakes his head*) I don't go along with you there, Mr. Jefferson. Why spend Government money — our tax money — on educating people who don't need to know how to read or write? Take a man like the owner of this little inn, for example. Why is it necessary for him or his wife to know how to read and write?

JEFFERSON: Well, how can a man be a good citizen if he can't read the papers and know what's going on in the country, especially in times like these? How can he protect himself ——?

(*There's a sound of a horse's hoofs and wagon wheels coming to a stop off stage. Then Mr. Gower's voice is heard off stage.*)

GOWER: (*Calls*) Mary! Mary!

(*Mrs. Gower comes out of the front door.*)

MRS. GOWER: (*Calls*) Yes, Will? Leave the wagon right there. The boy will take it round to the barn. You're kind of late, aren't you?

(*Will Gower enters. He's dressed in rough clothes. He looks tired and worried.*)

GOWER: I couldn't help it, Mary. Afternoon, gentlemen. (*His voice brightens*) Oh, how do, Mr. Jefferson?

JEFFERSON: Anything wrong, Will? You look worried and upset.

146

GOWER: There's plenty wrong, Mr. Jefferson! I started out early this morning to sell my vegetables in town. You know we sort of depend on that money to help us out here. I took the short cut as usual, the road that crosses the river a few miles up above.

JEFFERSON: Why, Will! The bridge across that stream was washed away by heavy rainstorms last week. Didn't you know that?

GOWER: No, I hadn't heard about it.

JEFFERSON: But it was in the paper right after it happened, and this week again, Will. And there's a warning sign posted half a mile before you come to the bridge.

GOWER: That could be, sir. Only thing is, I can't read, nor can Mary. We don't take the paper, and that sign meant nothing to me.

147

MRS. GOWER: What did you do, Will, when you came to the place and saw that the bridge was out?

GOWER: I thought I could make the horse swim across and drag the wagon after him. But that horse has more sense than I have. He wouldn't put one foot into that swift water. So I had to drive nearly all the way back here and take the long road to town.

MRS. GOWER: You must have got there very late, didn't you, Will?

GOWER: Much too late, Mary. The shopkeepers had already bought their vegetables from the other farmers. I had to bring my load back home again, with hardly any sold.

MRS. GOWER: (*Presses her hands together*) Oh, Will! Those vegetables will be no good at all by tomorrow. And we need that money so badly! Let's see if any of them can be saved. (*Mr. and Mrs. Gower leave.*)

JEFFERSON: All that much-needed money lost, because Will Gower and his wife can't read! Well, Mr. Bridges, what do you think now?

BRIDGES: I'm ready to change my mind. You're right, Mr. Jefferson. Every person should have an education. My vote goes to you.

SANDERS: I agree with you now, too. I've decided something else as well. You're the kind of man we need in the House of Burgesses, Mr. Jefferson — a man who's ready to stand up for equal rights for all. You'll get my vote.

JEFFERSON: Thank you, gentlemen! I hope I can get more people to think my way.

CURTAIN

NARRATOR: Thomas Jefferson's ideas of what was good and right for all the people won him the election to the Virginia House of Burgesses. This was the time when the British Government was passing many laws which hurt the business of the colonists. More and more taxes were put on articles the colonists got from England. The Americans called these laws and taxes unjust. They declared that the King had no right to make laws for them or tax them without their consent.

Like other American colonists, the people of Virginia, too, declared they would not put up with such taxation. They decided to try to make the King change his mind by refusing to buy any goods from England. A look into Jefferson's home at that time will show you something that might have happened in many another colonist's home.

SCENE 2

Time: 1773
Place: A room in Jefferson's home

(*Jefferson and his wife, Martha, are entertaining
a small group of people. As the scene opens, the
men are talking together at one side of the room. The
women are gathered around Sue Potter, looking at
her dress.*)

SUE: Do you like it? I just had it made.

MARTHA: It's very pretty, Sue, and you look lovely in it.

SUE: Thank you, Martha.

NANCY: (*Feels the cloth*) It's very fine wool. This is not
English wool, I hope!

SUE: Of course not, Nancy! The wool came from our own
lambs. Father wouldn't let us order anything from
England, even if Mother and I wanted to — and we
don't.

MARTHA: What about your wedding dress, Sue? We don't
have silks pretty enough for a wedding dress here in the
colonies. Are you ordering that from England?

SUE: (*Firm*) Not even that, Martha! I'll be married in a dress made from our own wool too. What's more, all the refreshments at the wedding will come from our plantation!

JEFFERSON: (*Turns to women*) You women are wonderful! I must say you're doing more than your share to make King George come to his senses.

MARTHA: We women are just as patriotic, just as good Americans, as you men, Tom.

HENRY: That's a good thing, Martha. We can never win out against England unless we all stick together.

MARTHA: Patrick, why don't you men get after the merchants who are raising their prices on some goods? Because they know we won't bring in any more from England, they're putting unreasonably high prices on the goods they still have.

NANCY: (*Laughs*) We made one grocer feel sorry he tried to raise the price of the tea he had, didn't we? Do you know about Mr. Wells, Tom?

JEFFERSON: No, Martha didn't tell me. What did you do, Nancy?

(*The women làugh as they take turns telling the story.*)

NANCY: Why, Mr. Wells knows, of course, that we won't order any more tea from England until the tax is removed. So he raised the price of his tea about four times what it was before.

SUE: We wouldn't stand for that, Mr. Jefferson. So, last Thursday, five of us women visited his shop together. When he told us the price of his tea, we gave him a piece of our mind, first. Then ——

MARTHA: Then Sue and I grabbed his arms and held them tight behind his back, and ——

NANCY: And Kate and Betsy and I went behind the counter, and measured out his tea in small packages, and marked them with the correct price.

SUE: The old price, of course.

MARTHA: How he yelled for us to let go of his arms! I can still hear him!

(*They all laugh heartily.*)

HENRY: One angry woman is enough to take care of any man. I can imagine how alarmed Mr. Wells was when five of you got after him!

MARTHA: It served him right, Patrick! If he were a patriotic American, he wouldn't try to make us pay extra for English goods right now. (*To the women*) Come up to my room, Nancy and Sue. I want to show you a new dress of mine.

(*The women leave.*)

JEFFERSON: Yes, the women are taking on the fight shoulder to shoulder with us men. We may yet make the King and Parliament see reason.

(*There's a knock at the door. John Randolph opens it and walks in quickly, shutting the door after him.*)

JEFFERSON: Why, Cousin John! Come in! Glad to see you!

RANDOLPH: (*Angry*) I'm not sure I'm glad to be here, in your home!

JEFFERSON: What do you mean? What's happened? What have I done?

RANDOLPH: It's the way you've gone around, working people up, putting crazy ideas of resistance to the King into people's heads! Now, look how they go about insulting people!

HENRY: What happened, Mr. Randolph? Surely nobody in Virginia would purposely insult a man of your wealth and position.

RANDOLPH: It was that barber who owns the shop across the way from the courthouse. I went in for a haircut, and — you won't believe it! — he refused to work on me!

JEFFERSON: That's Sam Platt. I can't imagine his insulting any one. What reason did he give for refusing to cut your hair, Cousin John?

RANDOLPH: He declared he wouldn't cut my hair because I am on the side of the King, not the colonists. Imagine! He refused to cut the hair of John Randolph of Virginia!

JEFFERSON: Sam Platt is a fine, honest citizen. He believes that we all must stand up for our rights.

RANDOLPH: Our rights! Don't you suppose the King and the English Parliament know what's good for the colonies? Why are you hotheaded colonists always against the King? You're Englishmen, and you should obey your King.

HENRY: If we're Englishmen, why won't the King grant us the same rights as the Englishmen in England? Why should laws be made for us, and taxes laid on us without our consent?

JEFFERSON: To my way of thinking, Cousin John, we colonists are no longer Englishmen. Many of us were born here, not in England. Some of the older colonists just happened to be born in England. When they grew discontented with the way things were done there, they came to America.

RANDOLPH: Stuff and nonsense, Tom! Such talk will get you into serious trouble with England.

JEFFERSON: If I had my way, I'd draw up a set of resolutions telling the King that we Americans should be treated as free people.

RANDOLPH: You're a pack of rebels — you Virginians and these other troublemakers up in New England who are setting themselves up against the King. Stop this dangerous nonsense, Tom! I warn you! You'll lose your fight, and you'll all be hanged!

HENRY: The King's men would have some trouble finding and hanging all the Americans who feel as we do. If all the colonists stand together on this, maybe we can make the King see reason and win our rights.

RANDOLPH: I'll have no part in this dangerous foolishness! I'll take no chances of losing my lands and being hanged as a rebel! I'm selling my property, and moving to England to live — for good.

JEFFERSON: Then we'll have to carry on without you, John. And I know we'll win the right to govern ourselves!

CURTAIN

NARRATOR: The laws made by England against the colonies soon made the colonists realize it was necessary for all of them to act together. They decided that a law or an attack by the King's soldiers against one colony should be treated as an attack against all. Each colony sent men to a meeting to talk over ways and means of forcing England to listen to their demands. This meeting was called the Continental Congress, and it met in

Philadelphia. Jefferson was chosen as one of the delegates from Virginia.

Before going to the first Continental Congress, the delegates from Virginia decided to write out their demands so that they could talk about them at the Continental Congress. Jefferson was well known for his learning and for his ability to write well. He was chosen to put the Virginia statements on paper. When the second Continental Congress met, in June, 1776, Jefferson was chosen as one of five men to draw up a declaration of independence.

SCENE 3

Time: June, 1776
Place: Jefferson's room in the Graaf home, Philadelphia.

(Jefferson is seated at a long table. Some sheets of paper are in front of him and at four other places on the table. There's a knock at the door, and Mrs. Graaf enters.)

MRS. GRAAF: Please excuse me for interrupting your work, Mr. Jefferson.

JEFFERSON: Not at all, Mrs. Graaf. Come right in.

MRS. GRAAF: Is there anything I can do for you, sir? I know how important your work is, and I want to make sure you're comfortable.

JEFFERSON: Thank you. I'm quite comfortable. I'm expecting some gentlemen here soon. Will you show them the way up here at once, please?

MRS. GRAAF: (*Goes to door*) I think I hear the men in the hall downstairs now, sir. I'll go right down and direct them to your room.

> (*She leaves. A few seconds later John Adams, Benjamin Franklin, Roger Sherman, and Robert Livingston enter. Jefferson rises to greet them.*)

JEFFERSON: Good morning, gentlemen! You're right on time.

> (*The men say good morning to Jefferson as they walk to the table.*)

FRANKLIN: I see you have paper and pens all ready for us, Jefferson. We'll try not to waste this paper.

JEFFERSON: (*Smiles*) Waste not, want not, as your Poor Richard says, Dr. Franklin.

LIVINGSTON: Besides, paper is hard to get in the colonies today, thanks to the King's laws and taxes.

ADAMS: Well, gentlemen, let's get down to the business on hand. Jefferson, since you were elected head of this committee, suppose you sit in the center, here.

> (*They all sit.*)

JEFFERSON: I don't know why I was voted this honor. You should be the head of this committee, Mr. Adams. You're older and wiser. I've been a silent member of the Congress.

ADAMS: It's true that you haven't made any speeches on the floor of Congress, Jefferson. But in your writing and in talk outside, you've shown yourself to be a man of excellent education and clear-headed thinking.

FRANKLIN: Your writings on government have been handed around among us. We all like your straight thinking, and clear way of expressing your thoughts, so that every man can understand.

ADAMS: That's why I gave you my vote, and did everything I could to make others vote for you.

SHERMAN: I did my best to have you chosen for this task, too, Jefferson.

JEFFERSON: Thank you, gentlemen. I'll do as well as I can. My heart is very much in this idea for a declaration of independence from England. (*He picks up some sheets of paper.*) I've already drawn up a rough plan of the statements we should put into the declaration.

LIVINGSTON: Well, let's not be in too much of a hurry about it, gentlemen. Not all the members of the Continental Congress are agreed that we should declare ourselves independent. Some of us believe that such a declaration would lead to a war with England.

FRANKLIN: My dear Livingston, I'm sure there can be no question in any one's mind about the fact that the American colonies are already independent. As for a war with England, haven't there already been battles between the colonists and the King's soldiers? Aren't we carrying on a war with England at this moment?

SHERMAN: And a successful war, too.

ADAMS: It's a good thing, all the same, to put the facts of the case — our wrongs at the hands of the King — into plain words. Then the world can know the reasons why we're declaring our independence.

LIVINGSTON: Let's hear some of those statements of yours, Jefferson.

JEFFERSON: (*Looks at his notes*)   As Mr. Adams says, we should let other countries know why we refuse to live under the rule of England.   I believe, then, that our declaration should begin by saying that our respect for the opinions of other nations makes us give our reasons for separating from England.

FRANKLIN: Good! That sounds like a good way to begin.

JEFFERSON: Then I believe we should list all the unjust laws and taxes passed by England without our consent, and all the unfriendly acts against our colonies.

LIVINGSTON: That's it! Acts like forcing us to keep the English soldiers in our homes, and not allowing us to trade with other countries.

SHERMAN: I think we should also mention how hard we've tried to keep matters from reaching such a bad state.

LIVINGSTON: Yes, and how often we've asked the King and the English Government to change these unjust laws. You must also remember to put in that we think taxation without representation is unfair.

JEFFERSON: I can hardly forget that, Livingston.

FRANKLIN: This Declaration of Independence would be a good place to set down your ideas on the rights every man should have, under his Government. Your ideas on these rights have been well expressed in the past, Jefferson.

JEFFERSON: I still believe firmly in those rights, Dr. Franklin. I believe every man has an equal right to life, liberty, and the pursuit of happiness.

ADAMS: Gentlemen, I'm sure we can safely leave the writing of this Declaration of Independence in the hands of Thomas Jefferson. He has the ability to get to the heart of any matter and to write it out clearly.

FRANKLIN: We'll meet again three weeks from to day, to read over and discuss Jefferson's final writing of the American Declaration of Independence. Then it will be ready for us to present to the entire Congress.

JEFFERSON: You do me a great honor, gentlemen. This is a great and important task. I shall do my best to show the world that it is right and necessary for the American colonies to declare their independence from England.

CURTAIN

NARRATOR: Well, Thomas Jefferson shut himself into his room and worked hard for the next three weeks, drawing up the Declaration of Independence. When it was brought before the Continental Congress, some of the delegates thought Jefferson had stated things too strongly against the King of England. Several of these statements were softened, and a few were taken out altogether. But the most important part of the Declaration, the introduction, was left in and passed by the delegates as Thomas Jefferson wrote it. Today, in many countries in the world, people are inspired by this idea of Jefferson's:

All men are created equal and are born with certain rights which cannot be taken from them. Among these rights are life, liberty, and the pursuit of happiness.

THE END

Clara

Barton

Angel of the Battlefield

MRS. PARKER	MRS. CARVER
AGNES	DR. HAMMOND
RED CROSS NURSE	SOLDIER GUARD
CAPTAIN SANDS	HOSPITAL MAILMAN
BILL	LAWSON
JOE	FROST
TOM	PATCHEN
PETE	BARBER
CLARA BARTON	MRS. GOLAY
MRS. FALES	DR. APPIA
SOLDIERS	GEN. DUFOUR

Time: The present

Place: A field on the edge of a river

(*A few tents are set up in the field. In the background can be seen the river bank and a few trees with broken branches. Mrs. Parker and her daughter Agnes sit on stools outside one tent. Each has a blanket wrapped around her shoulders.*)

MRS. PARKER: Keep your blanket tight around your shoulders, Agnes, dear. You musn't get chilled.

AGNES (*Shivers a little*) I'm all right, Mother. You'd better be careful yourself. Is Dad very sick?

163

MRS. PARKER: The Red Cross doctor says he'll be all right in a few days. He got a bad chill trying to save the cows, when the flood washed the barn into the river.

(*A woman in Red Cross uniform enters. She walks over to Mrs. Parker and Agnes.*)

NURSE: Good morning, Mrs. Parker. Hello, Agnes. I'm glad to tell you that the Red Cross truck has just arrived with a load of clothing. I'm sure we'll have something to fit both of you.

MRS. PARKER: Oh, thank you, Nurse! You Red Cross people have been just wonderful to us! So many houses and barns along the river have been ruined or washed away by the flood. What would we have done for food and shelter and medicine without the Red Cross?

AGNES: You know, Nurse, I always thought the Red Cross helped only the soldiers in wartime.

NURSE: That was the purpose of the Red Cross when it was first started, Agnes, many, many years ago. But that was soon changed. The Red Cross goes to the help of all people who've been hit by other disasters besides war — floods or earthquakes, for instance.

MRS. PARKER: By the way, who started the Red Cross?

NURSE: Well, it was started over in Europe by Henri Dunant, a Swiss. But the American Red Cross was started by Clara Barton.

MRS. PARKER: During one of our wars?

NURSE: No, after our war between the states. But Clara Barton's work for the soldiers began after the first battle of the Civil War. She was working for the Government in Washington at the time. She saw the first troop trains rolling into Washington and she set to work.

CURTAIN

SCENE 1

Time: April 17, 1861
Place: The Senate, Washington, D.C.

(*The Speaker's desk is at the right, front. The seats face the desk, in a half circle. The room is empty when the curtain rises. Then Captain Sands enters at the back of the room.*)

CAPT. SANDS: (*Talks to the men outside, voice raised a little*) We'll have to put you men in here for a while. This room is the Senate Chamber of the United States. I'm telling you before you come in, so you'll be careful not to do any damage. All right, now!
(*The room is quickly filled with soldiers. They take any seat they can, falling into the seats as if they were dead tired. They carry no packs. A few have bandages on head or arm.*)

VOICES: Oh, my tired feet! It's good to sit down! It's mighty good to get out of that hot sun!

(*Capt. Sands gets up on the Speaker's platform. He slaps his hand hard on the desk several times for attention. The men quiet down.*)

CAPT. SANDS: At ease here, men, till I can get orders where your company quarters are to be.

BILL: Why didn't somebody here have that worked out before our company got to Washington?

JOE: They must've known this company was coming down from New England.

TOM: No tents, no houses for us to stay in!

PETE: No proper uniforms or clothing for us, either! Look at us! Woolen clothing in this Washington heat!

CAPT. SANDS: (*Weary tone*) It won't do you men any good to growl or complain. We just aren't prepared yet to receive troops here. Make yourselves as comfortable as you can till I find out where you're to go.

(*Clara Barton enters, with Mrs. Fales and Mrs. Carver. They carry large market baskets. The men sit up and stare in surprise as the women walk down the room to the Speaker's platform. Clara Barton steps up alongside Capt. Sands.*)

MISS BARTON: Good afternoon, Captain.

CAPT. SANDS: Say, men! Here's a woman who knows a soldier's rank!

MISS BARTON: (*Turns to men, smiling*) You'll never catch me making a mistake in a soldier's rank, boys! My father trained me in that. He was an Indian fighter in Ohio — Captain Stephen Barton.

JOE: (*Stands up*) Captain Stephen Barton! Say! Are you Miss Clara Barton, Ma'am?

166

MISS BARTON: That's right!

JOE: You were my teacher, back home!
Remember Joe Black?

MISS BARTON: Joe Black? I certainly do, though you've grown a lot since then. Is your spelling as bad as ever, Joe?

JOE: I'm afraid so, Miss Barton, Ma'am, though it ain't — I mean, isn't your fault.

PETE: Say, Miss Barton! Remember me? Pete Stebbins. I used to take care of the schoolhouse stove for you.

VOICES: (*Men stand up, eager to be recognized*) And me — Hank Bowie! I'm Tim Kelly! Remember Johnny Dunn?

MISS BARTON: Of course I remember you, boys! So many of you were my boys when I taught school in Massachusetts. I was down at the railroad station a while ago, watching the trains come in. That's how I learned this company was from up my way.

CAPT. SANDS: (*Smiles*) I'm Captain Sands, Miss Barton. Since you were smart enough to find out that your home boys were in this company, perhaps you can find out where they should go, now that they're here.

MISS BARTON: No, Captain Sands, I won't mix in your army business. That job is yours. These two friends of mine, Mrs. Carver and Mrs. Fales, and I will take care of the men till you get back.

CAPT. SANDS: Very well. Good day, ladies.

(*He salutes and leaves.*)

MISS BARTON: When I saw you get off the train, boys, I knew you'd need help. So I asked these ladies to come along with me.

MRS. FALES: Where's your baggage, boys? Still in the railroad station?

PETE: No, Ma'am. You see, when we changed trains from one station to another in Baltimore, we boys got into a fight with some men who believe the South is right in this war. Four of our men were killed, and a lot of us were wounded.

MRS. CARVER: So that accounts for the bandages on some of you!

PETE: Yes, Ma'am. And while we were fighting, our baggage got put on another train, by mistake.

MISS BARTON: And here you are in heavy woolen clothing in this Washington heat!

BILL: With nothing to change into, Ma'am!

JOE: Not even a change of socks, Ma'am!

MISS BARTON: When I saw you march out of the station without any packs, I thought something must have gone wrong. So I made a quick search of my own room, and asked Mrs. Fales and Mrs. Carver to hunt up whatever they could find. And here we are! Now, boys, what do you want?

VOICE 1: A clean handkerchief, please!

VOICE 2: A pair of socks, size eleven! Not wool, please!

VOICE 3: Two coat buttons, please!

VOICE 4: There's a rip in my coat sleeve. I'll sew it up myself, Ma'am, if you'll lend me a needle and thread.

MISS BARTON: You'll have them all, boys! We've brought torn-up sheets for handkerchiefs and bandages.

MRS. FALES: We have several sizes of socks.

MRS. CARVER: We have plenty of needles and any color thread you want.

MISS BARTON: Some of you boys come up and help hand things out. We women have something more important to do first.

JOE: Shucks, Miss Barton! You ladies aren't leaving us, are you?

MISS BARTON: I should say not, Joe! Our more important job is to take a look at those wounds. The bandages don't look too clean, or even properly put on. We'll attend to those wounds and see if any of you need hospital attention.

BILL: Say, Miss Barton! Back home they used to say you were scared stiff at the sight of blood.

MISS BARTON: (*Smiles*) I used to be, Bill. Right now I haven't the time to be afraid of blood. There's too much work to be done. Now, boys, get started on these supplies in the baskets. We women will start looking at those bandages.

BILL: Right, Miss Barton! Boys, how about a cheer for Miss Barton? Come on! Hip — hip —

VOICES: Hurray for Miss Barton! Hurray!

CURTAIN

(*The Red Cross nurse comes out in front of the curtain.*)

NURSE: That's how Clara Barton began helping the wounded soldiers. Soon she could be found in many places. She was in the tents behind the lines, bringing extra food, clothing, and medical supplies that people sent her in answer to her begging letters. She was at the spot where the ambulances transferred the wounded to the trains that took them to the city hospitals. Once in a while she managed to ride in one of those ambulances, caring for the wounded on the way.

But she was not happy. What she wanted most was to go out to the front lines, where she could give the wounded immediate care. She begged and begged for permission to enter the front lines.

SCENE 2

Time: July, 1862
Place: Office of Dr. Hammond, Surgeon-General of the Union Army

(*Dr. Hammond is seated at his desk, looking over some papers. There's a knock at the door.*)

HAMMOND: (*Looks up*) Come in!
(*A soldier enters. He stands just inside the door and salutes. Dr. Hammond returns the salute.*)

SOLDIER: Beg pardon, Dr. Hammond. That woman is here again.

HAMMOND: (*Shaking head, but not angry*) That woman again! I don't have to ask who it is. She'll never give up till she gets what she wants. Well, show her in.

SOLDIER: Yes, sir!

> (*He stands aside to let Miss Barton in, then leaves, closing the door after him. Dr. Hammond rises to greet his visitor.*)

MISS BARTON: (*Walks over to Dr. Hammond's desk.*) Good morning, Dr. Hammond.

DR. HAMMOND: Good morning, Miss Barton. (*They shake hands.*) How are you today? Won't you sit down?

> (*They both sit down.*)

MISS BARTON: Dr. Hammond, I've just been riding to the hospital with some wounded soldiers. Hundreds were brought to the hospital today.

DR. HAMMOND: I'm afraid, Miss Barton, there'll be hundreds more before this war ends. We can only hope they'll recover with hospital treatment.

MISS BARTON: These are the lucky ones. They managed to stay alive till they reached the hospital. I'm upset about the others, the ones who might have had a chance, if they'd been taken care of sooner.

DR. HAMMOND: It's a sad thing that some of the wounded reach the hospital too late for help, or don't get there at all.

MISS BARTON: Too late! These are dreadful words, Dr. Hammond! We know so many of the boys can be saved, if they are taken care of right away. But after a battle, the wounded men lie on the field for hours — sometimes for a day or two — before they are picked up and placed in the ambulance. Then they have the long, rough trip to the hospital. It's this waiting time that's so dangerous. You know time can mean the difference between life and death for a wounded man!

DR. HAMMOND: Yes, I know. But what can we do, Miss Barton?

MISS BARTON: I've told you what I want you to do, Dr. Hammond. Give me a pass to the front lines, where medical supplies and help are needed most, and needed quickly.

DR. HAMMOND: Aren't you doing enough now, helping the men in the ambulances and in the hospitals?

MISS BARTON: No, Dr. Hammond! I want to be up in the front lines with the doctors. I can be of greater help there. Give me a pass to allow me to go right up front! Please!

HAMMOND: But, Miss Barton! How can we allow a woman to go up to the battlefield? It's no place for a woman!

MISS BARTON: It's no place for a man, either, Dr. Hammond. I hate war! But since there is a war, I must do everything I can to relieve some of the suffering. If I can't be a soldier myself, I can at least help the soldiers. Give me the pass, please, sir!

HAMMOND: You win, Miss Barton! (*He takes up a pen and reads as he writes.*) "Miss C. H. Barton has permission to travel in ambulances in any direction — for the purpose of distributing comforts for the sick and wounded — and nursing them — always under the direction of the surgeon in charge." Now I'll sign it. "William A. Hammond, Surgeon-General of the United States Army." Here! You have your pass, Miss Barton.

MISS BARTON: (*Takes the paper from him quickly and rises to go*) Thank you, Dr. Hammond! You are saving many lives.

HAMMOND: Some day your country will reward you, Miss Barton, for your unselfish work for our soldiers.

MISS BARTON: I want no reward from my country, Dr. Hammond. My greatest reward is a smile from a soldier whose pain I have helped relieve.

CURTAIN

(*The Red Cross nurse comes out in front of the curtain.*)

NURSE: By March, 1865, the end of the war between the states was in sight. Through the four long years of the war, thousands of men on both sides, the North and the South, had been moved around from one part of the country to another. Thousands had been killed. Some still lay wounded in some hospital, either on their own side or the enemy's side of the line. Some were held in prison. Many families didn't know what had become of their men who had gone to war. Then Clara Barton took on another task.

SCENE 3

Time: March, 1865
Place: A large room in a hospital in Washington, D.C.

(*Several men are sitting on cots or chairs. Some are reading books or newspapers. Others are writing letters. After a few seconds, a man in uniform enters. He is carrying a mailbag over his shoulder. Others look up.*)

MAILMAN: (*Calls out*) Mail's in! Anybody interested in mail?

VOICES: Got anything for me? Hand it out! Hurry up, will you?

MAILMAN: I wish you'd tell your friends to write postcards not letters. I can't read through envelopes.

LAWSON: (*Impatient*) We heard that joke before! Come on! Make it quick!

MAILMAN: Take it easy, Lawson! You'll enjoy it more when you get it. (*He takes some letters out of his bag and begins to call off names. He walks along the line of chairs as the men answer. Those who receive mail begin to read.*) Roberts! Patchen! Hood! Frost! Barber! Lawson! Two for you, Lawson.   That's all today, men.

> (*The man leaves. For a few seconds the men read their mail. Lawson puts one letter down with a sigh, and turns to Frost, in the next chair.*)

LAWSON: Another letter from my parents, begging me to try to find out what's happened to my young brother, Dick.

FROST: Is he in the army, too?

LAWSON: Yes. He joined up as a drummer boy two years ago.

FROST: How old was he?

LAWSON: Only fifteen, but my parents couldn't keep him out of it. Four months ago they received word that he was missing in action. A friend of his wrote that he thinks Dick was taken prisoner. But we haven't heard a word from Dick himself.

PATCHEN: (*On the other side of Lawson*) There are lots of letters in the papers from people who haven't heard from their men folks for a long time.

BARBER: There must be thousands of our men in prisons down South, and their families know nothing about them. The same goes for the Southern prisoners up North, too, I guess.

FROST: Well, the war'll be over soon. According to the paper, General Grant has Lee surrounded at Richmond.

PATCHEN: Lee will have to surrender, and when he does, it'll be all over.

LAWSON: Maybe, when prisoners are exchanged, we'll find my brother, Dick.

(*Miss Barton enters. The men wave to her.*)

VOICES: Hello, Miss Barton! Morning, Miss Barton!

LAWSON: Here's Miss Barton, the Angel of the Battlefield!

MISS BARTON: (*Smiles and waves to the men*) Come now, boys! I'm in no hurry to become any angel! I've work to do down here on earth.

FROST: We don't know where a small person like you gets the strength for all the work you do, nursing us soldiers, and cooking for us, too.

BARBER: I'll never forget the apple pie you made specially for me, just because I said I'd love some pie like my mother used to make.

LAWSON: The war's nearly over now. Why don't you go home and rest, Miss Barton?

MISS BARTON: What? You want me to desert the army now? As a matter of fact, boys, I've just started on a new task.

FROST: For us soldiers, I bet!

MISS BARTON: No, for your families, this time. I'm going to try to find missing brothers and husbands.

LAWSON: Like my brother Dick! How will you go about it, Miss Barton?

MISS BARTON: Well, with the help of some friends, I've set up an office to try to track down all these missing men. We'll try to get in touch with other soldiers in their company, or people in towns near where battles were fought. We've sent lists of names of the missing men to newspapers all over the country, and we're going to check hospital and prison records everywhere.

PATCHEN: That's wonderful! Did you get the Army to give you permission to carry on this work?

MISS BARTON: The Army? I didn't ask any General for permission. I went directly to the Commander in Chief, President Lincoln himself.

LAWSON: (*Smiles*) Leave it to you to go straight to the top!

MISS BARTON: The President has given his support to my plan, and allowed me to print his note of approval in the papers.

FROST: But this will be a long, difficult task! You must be all worn out, after all these years of war work, right in the front lines!

MISS BARTON: I'll find the strength somehow, boys. I can't rest while one soldier suffers in some hospital or prison or lies in an unmarked grave.

CURTAIN

(*The Red Cross nurse comes out in front of the curtain.*)

NURSE: The war between the states ended in April, 1865. But Clara Barton kept up her task of looking for missing soldiers. She traveled around the country, talking to people, checking hospital and prison records several years longer. At last this extra strain, after her years of work on the battlefields and in hospitals, broke her health entirely. She became very ill. The doctor ordered her to drop all work for three years. When she grew strong enough to travel, she went to Switzerland to rest. And that's where Clara Barton first heard of the Red Cross Society.

SCENE 4

Time: March, 1869
Place: Geneva, Switzerland

(*Clara Barton is resting in a large armchair, her feet on a footstool. She looks tired and weak. There's a knock at the door, and Mrs. Golay enters.*)

MRS. GOLAY: Good morning, Miss Barton. How do you feel today?

MISS BARTON: Good morning, Mrs. Golay. Still a little tired and weak, thank you, though my voice is getting stronger.

MRS. GOLAY: You really had no right to work yourself so hard. The doctor's right in ordering you to do nothing but rest for the next three years.

MISS BARTON: Resting is very hard work for me. I'm not used to it.

MRS. GOLAY: Well, just rest one day at a time, and don't think of the days ahead. I don't like to ask you, Miss Barton, but do you feel strong enough just now to receive visitors?

MISS BARTON: Visitors! Oh, no!

MRS. GOLAY: But these are very important men — Dr. Appia and General Dufour. They've been very anxious to meet you ever since they heard you were in Switzerland.

MISS BARTON: Well — I can't refuse to see them. Ask them to come in.

(*Mrs. Golay walks to the door and opens it.*)

MRS. GOLAY: Come in, gentlemen. Miss Barton will see you.

(*Mrs. Golay leaves as Dr. Appia and Gen. Dufour enter. The men shake hands with Miss Barton.*)

DR. APPIA: How do you do, Miss Barton? I am happy that you feel well enough to see us. I am Dr. Appia. This is General Dufour.

MISS BARTON: Forgive me for not rising to greet you, gentlemen. I'm still on the sick list. Sit down, please.

(*The men sit down near Miss Barton.*)

GEN. DUFOUR: Miss Barton, we've come to ask you if you can tell us why your great country, the United States, is not a member of the International Red Cross Society.

MISS BARTON: The International Red Cross Society? What's that?

GEN. DUFOUR: (*Surprised*) You have not heard about the Red Cross Society?

MISS BARTON: The Red Cross Society? No. What is it?

GEN. DUFOUR: You, Miss Barton, after all the magnificent work you did for the wounded in your war, you don't know about the Red Cross?

MISS BARTON: I've been ill for a long time, General. That may be one reason why I haven't heard about it. Please, tell me about it.

DR. APPIA: The Red Cross was formed for the purpose of relieving suffering in war. I was a doctor in the war of France and Austria against Italy. I tried to help many wounded men.

MISS BARTON: And I tried to help them in our war between the states, so I, too, know how much suffering there is in war.

DR. APPIA: That's why we've come to you now. The Red Cross was formed to work out a plan to relieve, and perhaps prevent much of the suffering among the wounded. But to make this plan work for the good of all nations, every country must join it.

MISS BARTON: Just how would this Red Cross work?

GEN. DUFOUR: Among other things, we plan that all hospital buildings, all those who work in them, and all sick and wounded men in these shall be treated as neutrals.

MISS BARTON: You mean, they're to be treated merely as sick men, and the people who are helping to care for the sick are not to be treated as enemies?

DR. APPIA: Exactly! They should not be fired on.

MISS BARTON: That would be wonderful! How often our sick and wounded men have been fired on, and our hospitals destroyed by gunfire! We've had to rush our wounded, and our doctors and nurses into wagons and hurry them from the battlefield, to keep them from being fired on as enemies.

Henri Dunant

GEN. DUFOUR: Many countries have agreed that all the wounded and all those taking care of them must be protected.

MISS BARTON: This sounds wonderful, gentlemen! Who started this idea of the Red Cross Society?

DR. APPIA: Henri Dunant, a Swiss. He watched a battle, about ten years ago, and he was horrified at the suffering of the soldiers who lay there without medical attention. When he returned to Switzerland, Dunant worked to interest the governments of Europe in forming a society of all nations for the relief of the wounded.

GEN. DUFOUR: The first meeting of people from many nations was held in Geneva in 1863, Miss Barton.

MISS BARTON: Oh! Then that's probably why I didn't hear about the Red Cross. We were fighting our war between the states at that time.

DR. APPIA: We've come to you, Miss Barton, with the hope that you will tell your people all about it, so that your great country, too, will join the International Red Cross Society.

GEN. DUFOUR: Perhaps your countrymen don't understand that each nation has its own Red Cross Society. But they all agree to respect and carry out the rules of the Geneva Treaty in time of war.

MISS BARTON: But how will these Red Cross workers be recognized on the battlefield, gentlemen? Will they have some password, or wear some special uniform?

DR. APPIA: Look at this, Miss Barton. (*He takes a small Red Cross flag out of his pocket.*) This is the flag and the sign of the Red Cross — a red cross on a white field. It will be painted on the ambulances and hospital buildings, and the workers will wear this sign on their uniforms. All nations throughout the world, we hope, will come to respect and obey the rules of the Red Cross.

MISS BARTON: I'm curious. Why did you choose this sign?

DR. APPIA: Henri Dunant, who started the idea of a Red Cross Society, was a Swiss, and the first meeting of the society was held in Switzerland. We decided to honor both the man and the country by using the colors of the Swiss flag. As you know, the Swiss flag is a white cross on a red field.

GEN. DUFOUR: Well, Miss Barton, now that you know what the Red Cross Society stands for, will you help persuade the United States to join it?

MISS BARTON: I most certainly will, gentlemen! Just as soon as my health permits, I'll go back to the United States and work with all my heart to have our government join the International Red Cross.

DR. APPIA: Good! We knew you'd understand and help, Miss Barton! And now we'll leave you. I'm afraid we've tired you out.

MISS BARTON: (*Sits up with great energy*) Wait, gentlemen! War is a terrible thing for soldiers. But what about those who aren't in the battle itself? What about the old men, the women, the children?

GEN. DUFOUR: War is hard on those at home, too, of course. But they don't suffer from wounds on the battlefield.

MISS BARTON: I'm thinking especially of those whose homes are destroyed, or whose fields are ruined by gun-fire. Aren't they, too, sufferers from the disaster of war?

GEN. DUFOUR: Most certainly.

MISS BARTON: Then why shouldn't they, too, be helped by the Red Cross? And what about people who are struck by other kinds of disasters — floods, or earthquakes, or disease that hits great numbers of people in some country? Why shouldn't the International Red Cross bring relief to people in great disasters like these?

DR. APPIA: Truly, you have a great heart, Miss Barton! But the Geneva Treaty covers only the wounded soldier in time of war.

MISS BARTON: Then I shall work for an addition to the rules of the Treaty, to send help to any country, wherever a disaster may strike.

GEN. DUFOUR: That would be an even greater service to the world! But your first step, Miss Barton, must be to persuade your country to join the International Red Cross.

MISS BARTON: I promise you, gentlemen, that I shall work with all my heart and with all my strength, to persuade Congress and the United States to form an American Red Cross Society. Then America, too, will join in bringing help to all people in trouble, everywhere!

CURTAIN

(*The Red Cross nurse comes out in front of the curtain.*)

NURSE: Clara Barton kept her promise, but it took a long time to do it. After an illness of many years, she finally managed to organize the American Red Cross Society. President Garfield nominated Miss Barton as the first president of that society. However, it took still more time to persuade the members of the United States Senate to agree to the treaty that would make the American Red Cross Society a member of the International Red Cross. The treaty was signed in 1883, fourteen years after Clara Barton had made her promise.

THE END

Robert E

Virginia's Valiant Son

CAST

MRS. LEE	BARBER
MILDRED	ROGERS
CUSTIS	JAMES
AGNES	PEASLEY
ROBERT E. LEE	ALTON
SOLDIER	GRADY
WILSON	CAPTAIN

SCENE 1

Time: February, 1861
Place: The Lee home in Virginia

(*Mrs. Lee, her son Custis, and the two daughters, all grown-ups, are in the living room. Mrs. Lee sits quietly sewing. The others are restless. They go from one window to the other, or sit in a chair for a few moments, until General Lee arrives*)

MRS. LEE: Why don't you all sit down and busy yourselves with a book, or something? Hopping up and down won't bring your father home one minute sooner.

MILDRED: We're all anxious to know why President Lincoln sent for Father. It must be very important.

CUSTIS: Father said General Scott would be at the meeting, too.

AGNES: General Scott? He's Commander in Chief of the Army, isn't he, Custis?

CUSTIS: Yes, next to the President, of course.

MILDRED: Mother, do you suppose the President will send soldiers into the states that have left the Union?

MRS. LEE: (*Troubled*) There's been no talk of that yet, thank Heaven! We can only hope and pray that President Lincoln won't feel he has to send soldiers against any state.

CUSTIS: Well, South Carolina said she'd secede from the Union if Lincoln became President, and she did.

MRS. LEE: There are other states down South that don't approve of Lincoln's ideas. They don't believe that the national government should have the power to pass laws doing away with slavery in every state. Some people believe that each state has the right to make its own laws, particularly about slavery.

(*Lee enters at the side, unseen by his family.*)

CUSTIS: I think South Carolina had the right to secede after Lincoln's election last fall. Good for South Carolina, I say!

LEE: (*Coming forward, stern*) That's a very foolish and very thoughtless thing to say, Custis!

(*Agnes, Mildred, and Custis rise.*)

MILDRED: Why, Father! We didn't hear you come in.

MRS. LEE: Robert! You look troubled. Are matters so very serious?

LEE: More serious than you can imagine. More states have seceded from the Union. Mississippi, Florida, and Alabama have followed South Carolina's example.

MRS. LEE: (*Shocked*) Oh, no!

LEE: Yes. The states that have seceded have just formed a nation of their own. They're hoping other states will join them.

CUSTIS: Have they chosen a leader, or a President, Father?

LEE: The leaders of each state met and chose my friend Jefferson Davis as President of the new nation.

CUSTIS: Well, I still say it takes courage for these states to leave the Union. Why do you say I'm foolish, Father?

LEE: Because it's unbelievable that any state should break up the Union, Custis. It's unbelievable that any one state, or even a few states, would destroy the nation that so many great men worked to build. George Washington was one of these great men. Think how sorrowful he would feel if he could see how these states are wrecking the Union he worked so hard to build.

UNION STATES

SECEDING STATES

TERRITORIES UNDER FEDERAL CONTROL

AGNES: But these Northerners can't order us around, Father! They have no right to tell us that we must free our slaves!

MRS. LEE: Many of us in the South hate slavery as much as most of the people in the North do, Agnes. In his will, my father stated that all his slaves should be set free after he died.

LEE: Your mother and I hate slavery, too, as much as any Northerner. Only we believe that slavery can't be done away with by law overnight. It must be done gradually. Many of us down here believe that to change the manner of working our huge plantations too quickly will cause a lot of trouble.

MILDRED: What do you think will happen now, Father? Do you think this secession of some states will lead to war between the North and South?

LEE: A war between the North and South would mean the end of the Union. That would be a great disaster!

CUSTIS: Why, Father? We're sure we're right when we say the Government in Washington can't make any laws for us that we don't approve of. The men of the South are every bit as brave as those up North. We're sure to win!

LEE: Think what you're saying, Custis! We have good friends and relatives up North. A break between the two parts of our country would be like a quarrel within a family. Can you bear the thought of going out and shooting your own brother, or your cousin?

MRS. LEE: Oh! Your own sister lives up North, Robert!

LEE: I've thought of her, Mary, and I've thought of all the good friends we made when I was Superintendent of the Academy at West Point. In a war between the states, friend will be fighting against friend, brother against brother. It's too terrible to think of!

MILDRED: (*Covering her eyes, half sobbing*) Oh, don't! Don't talk like that, Father! What will happen to William and me? Will we have to give each other up, forever?

CUSTIS: (*Serious now*) William lives in New York! You two could never marry, Mildred! I never thought of war in this way before!

AGNES: (*Goes to Mildred and puts an arm around her shoulders*) Don't cry, Mildred! Maybe there won't be any war.

LEE: Pray Heaven there will not be! War is such a cruel thing! It separates and destroys families and friends. It fills our hearts with hate instead of love for our neighbors.

MRS. LEE: What will you do, Robert, if more states secede from the Union, and war between the states should come?

191

LEE: (*Greatly troubled*) I don't know, Mary! I don't know! I love my country. It's unthinkable that the Union should be broken up. The idea of secession is dreadful! It's rebellion against our country!

MRS. LEE: Yet — suppose our own state should decide to secede? Suppose Virginia leaves the Union, Robert? What will you do?

LEE: (*Walks up and down as he talks*) That's what keeps going round and round in my mind all day and all night, Mary. What is the right thing for me to do? The thought of breaking away from the Union is dreadful. Yet if Virginia should secede and I remain with the North, I'd be deserting my own state. I'd have to fight my beloved Virginia.

MRS. LEE: It's a terrible decision you have to make! You're an officer of the United States, and by duty bound to defend it.

LEE: But how can I take up arms against Virginia, my own home? To which do I owe my greatest loyalty — Virginia, my home, or the United States, my country? It's so hard to decide, Mary!

MRS. LEE: Perhaps you won't have to make any decision, Robert. Perhaps Virginia won't leave the Union.

LEE: We can only hope that I won't have to make the choice between my own state and the Union. We can only hope and pray!

SCENE 2

Time: April, 1861
Place: The Lee home

(Mrs. Lee and Mildred are seated in the living room. Mrs. Lee is sewing. Mildred holds a book open, but she is not reading. Now and then she wipes her eyes with her handkerchief.)

MRS. LEE: *(Speaks gently, purposely not looking at Mildred)* Is your book interesting, Mildred dear? I haven't had a chance to read it yet.

MILDRED: I — I don't know, Mother. *(Sobbing)* Oh, Mother! William and I said good-by to each other this morning. He went home to New York, to join the Northern army.

MRS. LEE: I'm sure he'll come back to you when the war is over, dear.

MILDRED: He promised he would, but how can I be sure? Maybe — maybe — no, I won't even think of things that could happen.

MRS. LEE: Let's hope this war will be over very quickly.

MILDRED: *(Wipes her eyes and sits up bravely)* How silly of me to worry whether a man will marry me or not! What is that compared with Father's worries? Poor Father! He hardly ate a mouthful tonight. He hasn't spoken a word to any one since he received the news this afternoon that Virginia voted to secede.

193

MRS. LEE: He's been in his study all evening, struggling with his·conscience. He's trying to decide where his loyalty belongs — to the United States, or to his own home state. (*Lee enters. He looks pale and tired. Mildred rises and pulls a chair closer to her mother.*)

MILDRED: Sit down here, Father. (*She goes back to her own chair.*)

LEE: Thank you, my dear. (*He sits down wearily.*)

MRS. LEE: (*After a slight pause, gently*) Well, Robert?

LEE: (*Sits up straight and squares his shoulders*) I've made my decision, Mary.

(*Mrs. Lee and Mildred lean forward anxiously.*)

MRS. LEE: (*Quietly*) Is it the Union, Robert, or Virginia?

LEE: (*Quietly, but showing strain*) I've searched my heart, and I find there is only one loyalty for me above all others. That is to my beloved Virginia, my home. (*He sinks back wearily in his chair again.*) I have chosen to stand with Virginia.

MILDRED: Oh, Father! What will happen to all of us?

MRS. LEE: Have you thought out everything this means to you, to your own life?

LEE: It means that I shall never again wear the sword of an officer of the Army of the United States. I have just sent in my resignation to the Secretary of War.

MILDRED: And you could have been the Commander in Chief of all the Union Armies!

LEE: If I had chosen to stay with the North for that reason, Mildred, it would have been a selfish decision, made only to gain glory for myself. I could never square such a decision with my conscience.

MRS. LEE: That would not be your true self speaking, Robert. You couldn't do anything vain or selfish.

LEE: I hate slavery, as you do, too. We've freed our own
slaves. But I can't stay with the North just because
of that. We are at war now, the North against the
South. I know Northern soldiers will be sent into
Virginia. How could I lead an army into Virginia as
its enemy? I must defend my state, my home.

MILDRED: Oh, but it won't be for long, Father! We'll win
this war very quickly. All our young men are so eager
to get in and fight. Volunteers are pouring into Richmond.

MRS. LEE: Even our own two boys, Rooney and Custis,
have already enlisted in the Southern Army.

195

LEE: I'm not so sure the war will be over quickly. We are now eleven states against twenty-three in the North. We have hardly any factories. I don't know where our cannon and ammunition and muskets are to come from, or our shoes and uniforms, either.

MRS. LEE: Won't the European countries send us these supplies? After all, they need our cotton.

LEE: I'm not sure they'll be able to get into our ports. The Union ships will probably try to blockade our ports.

(There's a knock at the door. Mildred goes to open it. A soldier enters and salutes. Lee rises and returns the salute.)

SOLDIER: A message for Colonel Robert E. Lee, from President Davis.

LEE: Let me have it, please.

(The soldier gives Lee an envelope. Lee takes a sheet of paper out of the envelope and reads it quickly.)

You may tell President Davis that Colonel Lee will report to him in Richmond tomorrow morning, as requested.

SOLDIER: Yes, sir! *(He salutes and leaves.)*

MRS. LEE: What is it? What does Mr. — I should say, *President* Davis want you for? Does he say?

LEE: President Davis has appointed me to the post of General in command of all the troops in Virginia.

MRS. LEE: Oh, Robert! Then you can still wear the sword of an officer!

LEE: Yes, but an officer of the Southern Confederacy. I shall not be entering Virginia at the head of enemy troops. I am staying to defend my home!

SCENE 3

Time: April 5, 1865
Place: A field outside Appomattox Courthouse

(*Soldiers are gathered in groups. At the back of the stage is the house of Mr. McLean, where General Grant and General Lee are discussing the terms of Lee's surrender.*)

WILSON: Is it really true? Is General Lee really ready to surrender the Army of Northern Virginia?

BARBER: It's true, all right. He's in that house, talking terms with General Grant.

197

ROGERS: (*Angry*) Why is he surrendering? We can keep up the fight.

JAMES: (*Angry*) Surrender our army? How can he? We must never surrender to those Yankees!

PEASLEY: Will you tell me how we can go on fighting? We're starving, and you know it. We haven't any food even for our horses.

ALTON: I'm as brave as any of you, but we may as well admit it when we have nothing to fight with. Besides, the Union Army outnumbers us about five to one. They've surrounded Richmond.

GRADY: We can keep up the fight in the woods, in small bands of men. Lee should never surrender!

CAPTAIN: (*Above grumbling voices*) Listen, all of you who are talking against surrender! Do you think General Lee would surrender his men without good reason, unless he felt mighty sure there was no hope for us? Would General Lee ever run away from a fight? Has he ever been a coward?

VOICES: No! Never! Lee's no coward!

CAPTAIN: Whenever anything has gone wrong and we lost a battle, did General Lee ever blame his men or any other officer?

PEASLEY: No! He always took the blame for any mistake himself, no matter whose fault it was.

ALTON: He always protected the officers whose mistakes made us lose a battle.

CAPTAIN: Then you ought to realize that if General Lee has decided it's necessary to surrender our army, it's because he believes it's useless to keep up the fight. It's because he wants to prevent any more of us from being killed in a hopeless cause.

BARBER: If General Lee believes our cause is hopeless, then the South is licked for good. He loves the South. He has given up more than any of us to fight for it.

WILSON: If General Lee has given up, then all of us are through. He represents the South to us. We've come to look at the cause of the South as Lee's cause. We have fought for General Lee, himself, as much as for the South.

ROGERS: That's true. Lee stands for our cause, for our country, for everything we love.

CAPTAIN: Yes, we've fought for Lee because he is our beloved leader, because we've learned to love and admire him so much.

GRADY: That's all very well, Captain. Sure we admire and love General Lee. But what happens to us now, after he surrenders to the Yankees? How will we live? Tell me that!

JAMES: Yes! What will we do now? Our towns are destroyed, our farms ruined, our homes burned. How can we live with the Yankees who did this, when the war is over?

ROGERS: The Yankees will expect us to come back into the Union. How can we live with our enemies? We hate them too much.

(General Lee and two officers step out of the front door of the house. The men stop grumbling, raise their caps, and cheer him.)

VOICES: General Lee! Hurrah for Lee! General Lee!

(Lee holds up his hand to quiet the cheers. The noise dies down slowly.)

LEE: *(Salutes the men)* Thank you, men. I'm touched by your cheers when you all must know why I am here. I have just surrendered the Army of North Virginia to General Grant.

VOICES: *(Angry)* No! No surrender! No! No!

ALTON: *(Above the voices)* What are the terms of surrender, General?

LEE: General Grant's terms are very generous, far more generous than I ever hoped for. Officers and men may return to their homes. Those of you who own your own horses will be allowed to take them with you. General Grant generously said you will need them for your plowing. General Grant is also sending us several trainloads of food.

CAPTAIN: You see, men, not all Yankees hate us.

LEE: General Grant recognizes the splendid courage with which you have fought, though he may believe our cause was wrong.

GRADY: I say we have the courage to keep up our fight!

LEE: You have the courage. True! But you would be throwing your lives away. We must give in to greater numbers and greater supplies of food and ammunition. I feel it would be wrong to throw away the lives of more of our brave men in a hopeless fight.

ROGERS: Many years from now, what will history say of the surrender of this army, General Lee?

LEE: I cannot feel concerned about what history will say of me. That is not the question. The question is, is it right? I feel it is, and I am ready to take the responsibility.

VOICES: (*Cheers for Lee.*)

LEE: My friends, I have done the best I could for you. Now I must say good-by. It is very hard for me to say good-by. We have been through so much together, these past four years. You will take away with you the satisfaction of duty well performed.

(*The men crowd toward him, raising their caps.*)

VOICES: Good-by, General! God bless you, General Lee!

LEE: We are all full of sorrow for the way our fight has ended. The best way to cure this sorrow is to work towards wiping out the hatred we now have for our fellow countrymen. Go home and build up what has been destroyed. This means the love of your country, too. Remember, we now owe allegiance to the United States of America. When we are permitted to do so again, take the oath of allegiance, men, loyally and sincerely.

JAMES: General Lee, will you take the oath of allegiance to the Union?

LEE: Yes! I shall take the oath of allegiance to my country, the United States of America.

BARBER: Well, if General Lee takes the oath of allegiance, I say we should all take it.

LEE: From now on, we are one nation reunited. Pray Heaven the Union may never be broken again! We must work toward forgetting past hatred. We must try to heal all our war wounds, of the mind as well as of the body. And now, my friends, I must bid you an affectionate farewell. May God bless you and protect you always!

(*The men cheer and crowd around General Lee to shake his hand.*)

THE END

Jane

Addams

The Good Neighbor

CAST

ELLEN STARR	MR. COSTA
MRS. ADDAMS	MRS. HOFFMAN
MARY ELLWOOD	MRS. JENSEN
JANE ADDAMS	MRS. GOMEZ
MR. RILEY	MRS. RILEY
MR. GOMEZ	MRS. GRADY
MR. HOFFMAN	MRS. McBRIDE
MRS. COSTA	MEN

(Ellen Starr sits at a table, reading. She looks up and holds up the open book with the covers toward the audience.)

ELLEN: Jane Addams and I first became friends at Rockford Seminary. While she was there it was plain to see that she was unselfishly interested in others. When Jane finished at Rockford she decided to study medicine, so that she could work among the poor without pay.

But her first year at medical school was ended by a long and painful illness. When she had partly recovered the doctor ordered her to take a trip through Europe for a rest. That's how she happened to be in London late one Saturday night.

SCENE 1

Time: A Saturday night in 1882
Place: A hotel sitting room in London, England

(*Mrs. Addams, Jane Addams, and Mary Ellwood enter. They are wearing their hats and coats. Mrs. Addams and Mary are gay and excited, Jane is quiet. They remove their wraps as they talk.*)

MRS. ADDAMS: My! That was certainly an interesting trip through the London streets tonight, wasn't it, girls?

MARY: Yes, it was very exciting, Mrs. Addams. The city looks quite different by night.

MRS. ADDAMS: I guess any city looks different at night, Mary. I was thankful that we didn't have to live on one of those terrible East End streets.

MARY: So was I. Those people looked so frightfully poor and the streets were so dirty!

MRS. ADDAMS: I never saw such poverty! The people all looked so starved. And the awful food they were selling on those carts! You could see it wasn't fit to eat, yet the people were bargaining to get it for a few pennies.

JANE: (*Puts her hands before her face*) Don't! Oh, don't!

MARY: (*Worried*) What's the matter, Jane?

MRS. ADDAMS: (*Worried*) Aren't you feeling well, Jane dear? Was that jerky bus too much for your back?

JANE: No, I'm all right, thanks. It's only that I can't bear the thought of what we saw in the East End to-night. I didn't know there were such places!

MARY: It's certainly too bad that people have to live there. But why keep thinking about it?

JANE: I don't believe I'll ever forget the sight. The thin bodies, the starved faces, the workworn hands reaching for food unfit to eat!

MRS. ADDAMS: Don't work yourself up so much about strangers, Jane, dear. Remember, the doctor sent you here for a rest. After all, there's nothing you can do about this. You couldn't make all the poor people in the world rich, even if you gave away every cent your father left you.

JANE: I know that. But I can't help thinking what their homes must be like. Think of the children, living and trying to play in those dirty, crowded streets!

MARY: Why be so upset about these Londoners, Jane? We have plenty of poverty in our own United States.

JANE: I know, Mary. I remember, when I was about six years old, Father took me with him to one of his flour mills. We had to walk through the poor part of town, where the children were playing in narrow, dirty streets. The houses were small and ugly. I asked Father why people lived in such small, ugly houses. He told me it was because they couldn't afford anything better.

MARY: I suppose you asked your father to build pretty houses for all those children.

JANE: Not exactly. I told Father that when I grew up I'd live in a large house right in the middle of ugly little houses like those. Then I'd ask the poor children to come and play in my big yard.

MRS. ADDAMS: That's just like you, Jane! That's why you wanted to study medicine, too — so you could help others.

MARY: (*Smiles*) Well, would you like to settle down in London and build your big house right in the middle of those terrible houses in the East End?

JANE: Don't tease me about this, Mary, please! All these years, while I've been at college, I've felt that my life was empty. I must do something with my life, something worthwhile, something with a purpose. Now I know what that purpose is.

MRS. ADDAMS: What, Jane dear? Something for the good of others, I'm sure.

JANE: To fight poverty, Mother! To help people live like human beings. When I get back to Chicago, I'm going to find my big house among the small ugly ones, and I'm going to invite my neighbors in to enjoy it!

CURTAIN

(*Ellen Starr comes before the curtain, book in hand.*)

ELLEN: During her travels in Europe Jane Addams regained her health. She saw many handsome palaces and museums full of beautiful things. But no matter how many fine sights she saw, she couldn't forget those poor hands stretching out for food. She saw poverty in other countries besides England. It made her more certain than ever that she wanted her big house for her neighbors to enjoy.

Some years later, when she returned to Chicago, Jane asked me to help her find a suitable house. At last we found it. Hull House, named after the wealthy man who had built it many years before, was now badly run down. But it was large and comfortable, with wide halls, a porch on three sides, and a bit of green lawn. It was in a neighborhood of dirty factories and tenements crowded with poor people.

Jane furnished Hull House as she would have furnished her own home. The furnishings were simple, but comfortable and in good taste. On September 18, 1889, Jane Addams, her housekeeper, Miss Keyser, and I moved in. We opened the door of Hull House and invited our neighbors to visit us. But the neighbors were slow to come.

SCENE 2

Time: October, 1889
Place: Halsted Street, Chicago

(*The background shows the lower floors of some tenement houses on a city street. Some poorly dressed people are sitting out on the sidewalk, on broken chairs or wooden boxes.*)

RILEY: Any of you been visiting our new neighbors across the street yet?

GOMEZ: You mean over in Hull House, Riley? Not me!

HOFFMAN: It's very strange. Why should a rich woman like that Miss Addams move into a big house on our poor street?

MRS. COSTA: That's what lots of us want to know. What does she want here?

COSTA: Two women and a housekeeper to work for them, in that big house, and us with a family of children crowded into two little rooms!

RILEY: Why do they invite us to visit them? That's what I can't understand. What's back of it? I don't trust 'em!

MRS. HOFFMAN: You think maybe these rich ladies are here only to see how we poor people live?

MRS. JENSEN: Maybe they try to get into Heaven by giving us poor people a cup of tea, or a loaf of bread on holidays.

RILEY: Charity! I don't want their charity, or their pity, either! That rich Miss Addams won't give *me* a cup of tea and pat herself on the back! I have my pride, I have!

COSTA: Those women could be spies, to help the police when any of us gets into trouble.

GOMEZ: Or spies for the factory owner, maybe, to see if we're forming a union to fight for better pay.

HOFFMAN: My wife and I came to America because in my old country people of my religion weren't allowed to work in some kinds of business. We couldn't study to improve ourselves. Do you think these rich ladies invite us to their house so they can try to change our religion?

RILEY: I'd like to see them try! America's a free country. We can have any religion we want, here!

MRS. GOMEZ: Well, they can't drag us into their house. We don't have to go if we don't want to.

MRS. COSTA: That's right. (*Somewhat longingly*) But — it looks beautiful from outside, doesn't it?

MRS. RILEY: That it does! I saw the most elegant furniture going into it. Sofas and chairs that looked mighty soft and comfortable. I wonder what it feels like to sit in them?

GOMEZ: The plumber down the block helped fix things in there. He says they have a bathroom in the house. It's the only bathroom for a mile around.

MRS. HOFFMAN: They say there are lots of fine pictures on the walls, and all kinds of nice things she brought from Europe. I wonder if she has any dishes from Germany?

MRS. COSTA: In Italy we have beautiful things, too. I used to go to the museums, to look at fine pictures.

RILEY: Say! You women really mean you'd like to visit those swells in Hull House? I don't trust 'em, I say!

MRS. RILEY: Now Joe, don't you get so hot under the collar about those rich women in Hull House. Why, your own sister Bridget goes there to listen to music on that new-fangled phonograph.

RILEY: She does?

MRS. RILEY: Uh huh. And she says that Miss Addams and Miss Starr are fine people. They don't put on airs at all.

MRS. COSTA: I didn't like to tell it before, but my sister Maria had to deliver some curtains there. Maria said the ladies were just as nice as poor women. They showed her around, and they even talked Italian to her. They lent her a book that she wanted to read.

MRS. HOFFMAN: Maybe they would explain some things about America to me. There is so much I would like to understand.

HOFFMAN: And if we understand better, then we can be better Americans.

MRS. RILEY: Well, maybe I'll drop in at Hull House some day when the factory has no work for me to take home.

MRS. COSTA: I'll go with you, Mrs. Riley. It isn't right that we should be standoffish just because they're rich.

MRS. RILEY: You're right! I wonder if they know how to make a proper cup of tea?

CURTAIN

(Ellen Starr comes in front of the curtain.)

ELLEN: Yes, at first the poor people of that neighborhood didn't know what to make of Jane Addams, the "strange woman" who moved into "the big house" among the dirty, crowded tenement houses. No rich, educated people had ever taken any interest in them before, and they wondered what Miss Addams' hidden reason could be. Little by little, however, the more adventurous began visiting Hull House. They came because they were curious. They kept on coming because they got what they wanted and needed.

SCENE 3

> *Time:* A week later
>
> *Place:* The living room of Hull House

(*A few comfortable sofas and chairs stand about,
with small tables beside them.   There are bright
pictures on the walls and white curtains at the
windows.   The door at the back is slightly open.
There's a knock at the door.   After a few seconds
the door is pushed open and Mrs. Riley and Mrs.
Costa enter.   They look around.*)

MRS. RILEY: Nobody around, and the door left open! D'you
suppose it's all right for us to come in, Mrs. Costa?

MRS. COSTA: Maybe it'd be better to go out and knock on
the door again.

(*Jane Addams and Ellen Starr enter from the side.
Miss Addams is holding a broom.*)

JANE: Oh! Good morning, ladies. We didn't hear the bell. Come in and sit down, won't you?

MRS. RILEY: We didn't look for a doorbell. We don't have them in our houses, so we knocked.

MRS. COSTA: We were going out to knock again.

JANE: (*Laughs*) Don't worry about that, ladies. Our door is never locked, not even at night.

MRS. RILEY: You mean to say you don't lock your door at night?

JANE: Why, no. You see, the night before we were ready to open Hull House to our neighbors, Miss Starr and I — excuse me! I should have introduced Miss Starr before! I'm Miss Addams. Anyhow, Miss Starr and I were so tired out that night, from all the work we'd been doing, that we just fell into bed. The next morning we noticed that we had not only forgotten to lock the door. We had left it wide open.

ELLEN: And we've never locked our doors since.

MRS. COSTA: Well, I never! And nothing's ever been stolen?

JANE: (*Simply*) Who would want to steal from friends? Oh! Here I am, talking with a broom in my hand. Excuse me a moment while I put it back in the kitchen, Mrs. ——

MRS. RILEY: I'm Mrs. Riley.

MRS. COSTA: And I'm Mrs. Costa.

JANE: We're happy to have you here. I'll be right back.
(*She leaves.*)

MRS. RILEY: What's Miss Addams doing with a broom? She doesn't do any housework, does she?

ELLEN: Oh, yes. We both do, when there's work to be done.

MRS. COSTA: Rich women like you?

ELLEN: We had a sewing class here last night. Some girls from the furniture factory down the street are learning to sew their own clothes. A friend of Miss Addams' is teaching them. There's always extra cleaning to do after the sewing club meets.

(Jane Addams returns to the room.)

JANE: I was reading a book to the girls after the sewing lesson. They were so interested, we decided to form a reading club, too. I believe we can get the public library to set up a branch right here in Hull House.

MRS. RILEY: My husband's sister was telling us how much she likes to come here. To tell the truth, Miss Addams, Mrs. Costa and I just dropped in here to see if the place is as fine as Bridget keeps telling us.

MRS. COSTA: The neighbors are sure now that you haven't any secret reasons for coming here to live. At first some of them thought you might be spies for the police or the factory owners.

JANE: Well, goodness me! What ever put such notions into their heads, Mrs. Costa?

MRS. COSTA: You see, we're used to being cheated and lied to, so others can make money out of us. It's been kind of hard for us to make up our minds that all you want is to be neighborly, and to give us a good time, and maybe teach us something that'll help us in some way.

ELLEN: We're glad you came in to find out for yourselves that all we want is to be friendly, helpful neighbors. Why don't you come in some evening and bring your husbands?

JANE: Ask some of the other neighbors to come with you, too. We can find something to do that will interest every one of you.

ELLEN: The men can play checkers or work on some hobby they've always wanted to take up, or just talk about what's wrong with our country and how they would change things if they were President of the United States. That's a great American game!

JANE: We needn't tell you women what you'd like to do for a change from the cares of your own home.

MRS. RILEY: The cares — oh, my goodness! (*She gets up suddenly*.) I have to run home right now! I left the baby tied to the foot of the bed!

JANE: (*Shocked*) You tied the baby to the bed!

MRS. RILEY: Marty's not two yet. He's too young to walk all the way, and I can't carry him when I go to the factory to get a load of coats to sew buttons on. So I tie him to the bedpost with a long rope. Then he can't climb out of the window, or something.

ELLEN: But that's terrible! Suppose·a fire should break out, or some accident should happen in the building!

MRS. RILEY: I worry plenty about that, Miss Starr, I can tell you! But lots of us mothers have to do that when we go to work. I couldn't get any work today.

MRS. COSTA: My Rosina is five, so I let her stay on the street while I'm away.

JANE: We've got to do something about this! Mrs. Riley, tell the neighborhood mothers who work that they may bring their young children here, to Hull House. We'll take care of them while the mothers are at work.

MRS. RILEY: You'll mind our babies for us?

JANE: Yes. We'll have a day nursery for the very youngest and a kindergarten for those that are a little older but not quite old enough to go to school.

ELLEN: I know we can get more of our friends to come down here to help out.

MRS. RILEY: You'll mind the babies for nothing, Miss Addams? Just out of charity?

JANE: (*Smiles*) Oh, you needn't think I'm giving you charity, Mrs. Riley. The mothers will be asked to pay five cents a day, if they can afford it. If they can't, they may leave the babies anyhow. We'll take care of them as one neighbor might for another.

MRS. RILEY: Heaven bless you, Miss Addams! Imagine any of us thinking you came here with anything bad in your heart!

JANE: I guess we'd better not judge any of our neighbors, Mrs. Riley, until we really know them.

CURTAIN

(*Ellen Starr comes before the curtain.*)

ELLEN: Soon the neighbors began coming to Hull House in greater and greater numbers. Educated men and women who heard of the work of Hull House begged to be allowed to help. Jane Addams found herself in the middle of all the life of the neighborhood. Everyone who needed help came to Hull House — a mother with a sick child, a man out of a job, an old woman who couldn't pay her rent. They got the help they needed.

One of Jane Addams' hopes in starting Hull House was to help the neighbors of many different nationalities understand each other and live in friendship. She believed that if people of different nations could only learn to understand each other, there could be an end to hatred and war. And Hull House did its share in its own neighborhood. Sometimes the results were amusing and surprising. One day the Irish women decided to give a party for the Italian women. Invitations were sent out. The night of the party brought a surprise.

SCENE 4

Time: Several years later
Place: The large living room of Hull House

(*A number of women are moving about, talking to each other. They are wearing green dresses, white aprons, and green caps. Jane Addams and Ellen Starr are among them, but not in costume. At the side of the room refreshment tables are set up.*)

MRS. RILEY: It's nearly nine o'clock, Miss Addams, and not a one of those Italian women has shown up. We told them the party was to start at eight.

MRS. GRADY: I helped send out the invitations. There was no mistake about the date or the time.

JANE: Oh I'm sure there's no mistake anywhere about the date or the time. The women will be along pretty soon. There's no need to worry.

MRS. MCBRIDE: It would be a shame to waste half these refreshments. I baked the Irish raisin bread myself for the cheese sandwiches.

ELLEN: (*Smiles*) You'll find plenty of takers for those sandwiches, Mrs. McBride. Food never goes begging at Hull House!

(*The sound of many feet is heard outside the room.*)

JANE: They're coming now, ladies! Fix your caps and look your prettiest!

MRS. GRADY: I hope they're wearing Italian costumes.
(*The door opens. In come about a dozen men in ordinary street clothes. They stand around uncomfortably for a few seconds. Then Mr. Costa steps up to Jane Addams.*)

COSTA: Good evening, Miss Addams.   We are here.

JANE: (*Tries to hide her surprise*) Uh — so I see.   We're glad to have you.   But — where are the women?   Where are your wives?

COSTA: At home, of course.

ELLEN: At home?   But this party is being given for your women.

COSTA: That is not possible, at night, Miss Starr.

JANE: You mean, Mr. Costa, that the women have to stay at home to wash the dishes and put the children to bed?   Couldn't you men do that for just this night?

COSTA: You do not understand, Miss Addams. In Italy it is not nice for a woman to go out at night without her husband. Our wives wouldn't do such a thing. So they sent us to this party, in their place.

JANE: (*Helpless gasp*) Oh! We — we're rather surprised, that's all.

MRS. MCBRIDE: We were expecting the women. Now our party is off!

COSTA: Why is the party off? My wife, she said the Italian women and the Irish women were going to dance and have fun. What do you say the Italian men dance for you, the way they do in Italy?

MRS. RILEY: Say! That's not a bad idea at all! You dance an Italian dance for us, then we'll do an Irish jig for you!

JANE: Come on, gentlemen! What shall it be?

COSTA: The tarantella! We show you, ladies, then you dance it with us!

MRS. GRADY: Then we'll show you how to do an Irish jig!

JANE: And then we'll all dance an American dance together, like good neighbors! The party is saved! But next time bring your wives along, gentlemen!

CURTAIN

(*Ellen Starr comes before the curtain.*)

ELLEN: Little by little Hull House became part of the life of Chicago. Many new buildings had to be added to take care of the many clubs and workshops the young and old neighbors asked for. Jane Addams made it her business to give the neighbors what they needed. Other cities watched Hull House and set up neighborhood houses of their own, with the same idea of helpfulness.

Now Jane Addams began to feel that she was doing something worth while. But she never remained contented for long. Hand in hand with her neighbors she fought for better things, not only for them but for all people. She helped to get laws shortening the working hours of women in her own state. She fought for the right of women to vote. She was never afraid to join any movement that she believed just and for the good of all.

Today Hull House, with its many buildings, still helps its neighbors. It stands as a splendid monument to Jane Addams, the Good Neighbor.

THE END

Hull House today